# SHOCK
## AND
# AWE

STEPHEN McCUTCHAN

# SHOCK
## AND AWE

*How the Church Could End Racism*
*in the United States*

PRIMIX
PUBLISHING
THE WRITE CHOICE

Primix Publishing
11620 Wilshire Blvd
Suite 900, West Wilshire Center, Los Angeles, CA, 90025
www.primixpublishing.com
Phone: 1-800-538-5788

Published by Primix Publishing    01/12/2024

ISBN: 979-8-89194-048-2(sc)
ISBN: 979-8-89194-049-9(e)

Library of Congress Control Number: 2024900919

I dedicate this novel to my support team, who both supported me during the rough periods in my life and with my publishing efforts:
Daughter, Sonia Quinonez, and husband, Jose Quinonez.

And the best grandchildren in the world: granddaughter Cecilia Quinonez, grandson Alejandro Quinonez, and daughter, Nicole McCutchan.

I also dedicate it to the memory of Stokely Carmichael, who significantly affected my calling when I heard him speak at Union Theological Seminary in New York City.

In the middle of a lecture to mostly Caucasian seminarians, he said, *"I don't want you to come down to the ghetto to get rid of your guilt off my back. I want you to go out into the suburbs where the power of racism exists and confront it there."*

*"The Lord said to Cain, 'Where is your brother, Abel?' He said, 'I do not know; am I my brother's keeper?'" Genesis 4:10*

*"Then Jesus said, 'Father, forgive them; for they do not know what they are doing" Luke 23:34*
*Jesus drew this from Numbers 15:22-31.*

ESCÚCHEME

# INTRODUCTION

Presbyterian pastor Stephen McCutchan's anti-racist novel leaves readers in shock and awe.

The book reaffirms the message that God is not defeated by racism; we are when we refuse to obey the central command of Christ to love our neighbor as Christ loved us.

Presbyterian pastor Stephen McCutchan has a mission to address and fight racism, especially in the church, and promote peace, respect, and dialogue among members of different racial and religious backgrounds.

Pastor McCutchan's anti-racist message in this novel helps readers, most especially white Christians, fix their gaze on the suffering Christ in the wounds of their Black brothers and sisters. He said that his book *"Shock and Awe tells the story of what it might look like for a church to work through the fears and guilt of the racism in our society and grow spiritually on their journey. It becomes a parable for our contemporary church."*

Pastor Fred Livingood rushes to the hospital to support his Black pastor colleague Tony Southgate. He finds Tony facing the terror that most Black parents face. His son has been shot by Baltimore police officers and clings to his life.

The subject of racism becomes more than an abstract discussion. It is personal now, and Fred is determined to confront his largely Caucasian church about racism as a spiritual challenge. Churches don't like to have their comfortable faith disrupted, but Fred chooses to get creative and allow conflict to be fertile ground for spiritual growth rather than a threat.

Pastor McCutchan asks on his book's back cover, "Can you picture what it would be for a predominantly White church to address racism as a path to their own spiritual growth? What does it take for churches to engage each other and listen for God's whisper of reconciling the church to God's self and not counting their sins against them? What if God was inviting Christians to choose to journey across the wilderness of racism towards a Promised Land free of bigotry and prejudice."

Shock and awe should invite White Christians and all Christians, in general, to see Christ in those who suffer racism. Christians should recognize the fact that Black people, especially Black Christians, have been fighting against racism for a long time. Christians are exhorted to advocate for people who suffer racial prejudice while their neighbors look away in denial, pain, confusion, and guilt.

"If you have ever wondered how churches can creatively listen to God in the arena of racism, then this novel helps tell a possible story that can spark your imagination. You will also learn about how we can learn from South Africa about how our own version of the Truth and Reconciliation Commission can offer us hope for a reconciled world."

Purchase Shock and Awe: A Church Recognizes Its Racism and is Awed by God's Invitation by Stephen McCutchan today on Amazon or the author's website https://www.smccutchan.com/

# FOREWARD

## Written by Rev. Bobby Musengwa

Rev. Steve McCutchan is a lifelong, dedicated pastor, writer and thinker on issues of racial reconciliation and justice. His journey includes meeting with Stokley Carmichael in the late sixties, whereupon Steve got clarity on where to focus his energies on matters of racial reconciliation and justice issues.

Steve uses his imagination to confront real-life issues and problems facing people of faith. In his book, Shock and Awe, Steve highlights real problems facing a white pastor as he seeks to respond to a fellow black pastor who was facing a difficult situation with his son in a racist atmosphere. The human friendship these two pastors have allows them to be empathetic with one another, fostering understanding on the part of the white pastor regarding the overwhelming difficulties facing the black pastor, brought about by structural racism.

By using his imagination and fiction as literary tools, Steve succeeds in creating a non-threatening space for white people to confront the vagaries of racism with human eyes, fostering empathy and understanding. Moreover, Steve appeals to his Christian values, which emphasize reconciliation and justice, to invite Christians and other readers to respond to issues of racism and a cry for justice.

My congregation read this book and joined in weekly study sessions over several months. It was illuminating to those who participated, including new insights to wonderful, well-meaning white Christians who were able to see these issues of racism with new eyes. I appreciated Steve's innovative tool of using fiction as a literary device to foster understanding in serious, real life issues facing our church, community, nation, and world.

Such a strategy was used by literary giants such as Alan Patton in my home country of South Africa, when he wrote and published, "Cry, the Beloved Country." Steve's hope is to see more courageous policies developed, similar to the Truth and Reconciliation Commission of South Africa, which allowed truth-telling to expose the horrors of Apartheid racism, with the hope of bringing about healing and reconciliation among people and nation. May his prophetic, undying hope one day come to fruition.

Rev. Bobby Musengwa, Pastor, Maximo Presbyterian Church, St. Petersburg, Florida, USA (formerly from South Africa)


--

Rev. Bobby Musengwa
Maximo Presbyterian Church
3200 58th Avenue South
St. Petersburg, Florida 33712
727-867-2311 Office
727-480-4982 Cellular
maximochurch.com

# AUTHOR BIO

Stephen McCutchan has been an ordained Presbyterian pastor for fifty years. He lives in St. Petersburg, Florida.

Steve spent thirty-eight years in the pastoral ministry interpreting the Gospel to lay people who experience the tension of division in their world. For twenty-three years, he combined ministry with his middle-class congregation with monthly involvement in counseling the poor in his city. He helped found the Presbyterian Inter-Racial Dialogue that, in November 2012, celebrated twenty years of working with six Presbyterian churches, three predominantly black and three predominantly white, building a community that breaks down the barriers of racism. His book, Let's Have Lunch, Conversation, Race, and Community: Celebrating 20 Years of the Presbyterian Inter-Racial Dialogue, recounts that journey. He also helped establish a Hispanic ministry in Winston-Salem. His church has participated in regular activities with the Jewish community. Five times the church shared in an interfaith, interracial habitat that included Christians, Jews, and Muslims; Caucasians, Blacks, and Hispanics. He has been a featured speaker at Moravian, Catholic, Episcopal, Lutheran, and Presbyterian convocations.

He has led webinars on both writing and the care of clergy. He is also the author of Racism and God's Grace: Truth and Reconciliation for American Churches. Learn more about him, his works, and his thoughts by visiting his website **www.smccutchan.com**

# CHAPTER 1

# THE RECEPTION LINE

Pastor Fred Livingood pronounces the benediction and slowly makes his way to the main door of the sanctuary of Fourth Presbyterian Church. He feels the tenseness in the air and hushed conversation as they prepare to leave the sanctuary. Unlike most times, as he proceeds down the aisle, he notices that not as many people look up to catch his eye.

How do you greet people, many of whom were made to feel uncomfortable by his sermon, and not become defensive yourself by their brief responses at the door? What does the Gospel have to say to a people living in a society that is experiencing protests and racial incidents that have raised the temperature of social intercourse? He had struggled with this sermon and rewritten it several times this past week.

He hated conflict and worked hard to build good relationships within the church. Sometimes he worried that keeping the peace became more important than integrity. He loved the Scripture, but it often made him feel guilty. Sometimes some of Jesus's commands seem unrealistic in today's society. Jesus kept hanging around the wrong type of people and didn't seem to care if it offended people or not. He talked about it being easier for a camel to pass through the eye of a needle than a rich man to enter the Kingdom of Heaven

-- not exactly a comfortable message for some of his prosperous members. It's clear Jesus never managed a church and tried to meet the yearly budget.

Bertha Johnson approached him and held out her hand. At 87, she was still bouncy and cheerful. "Thanks for that challenging sermon today, Reverend. That took a lot of courage, but it held a lot of truth."

"Thank you, Bertha. I hope you've been feeling all right this week."

"Waiting for some medical tests to come back, but otherwise, I'm doing fine."

Several other people greeted him, some with smiles and some with frowns and head shakes, as they moved quickly out the door. He glanced down the line, and something inside him stiffened. It felt like a storm cloud was gathering, and he could almost hear the rumble of thunder.

Victor Bellinger was advancing towards him like a bull, having spotted the red flag and preparing to charge. The little boy inside him told him to run and hide, but he knew that wasn't an option. All he could do was stand up straight, stick out his hand, and say, "Victor, how are you today?"

"I felt better before coming here and had to listen to your political nonsense. If I wanted to get the news, I'd have stayed home and read the Wall Street Journal. I come here to hear good news and hope, not to be accused of being a racist and whatever else you spouted off in that poor excuse for a sermon." He was breathing hard and getting redder in the face with each word he spoke.

"Now, dear," his wife Marsha, an attractive blond of about 50 years of age, patted his arm. "Don't get so upset. It's not good for your blood pressure."

"I'm sorry you're upset, Victor. I'd be glad to talk with you further after I've finished talking to the others who are in line."

Victor's eyes narrowed, and his chin stuck forward. "Why wait. Maybe they want to see what a wuss you are. Why not put your money where your mouth is, Reverend? In fact, I might just talk to a few of the elders and see if they will agree to hold up your pay until you see the light. How does that sound, Reverend?"

Before Fred could respond, another voice spoke up, "It sounds to me like you think you can blackmail the pastor."

Fred looked toward the new speaker. It was Fran Smith, an African American teenager who had lately become part of the church youth group. This was one of the few times he'd seen her in worship. She had a fierce look on her face as if she were ready to take on the world.

All eyes turned towards her and then back to Victor to see how he would respond.

Victor got even redder in the face. "You watch your mouth, young lady. You are not part of this conversation. If your people knew how to behave, we wouldn't have all these problems."

Fred would never forget that moment, frozen in time. There was an audible gasp from several people standing nearby. Even Victor knew he had gone too far, but his words hung in the air.

Then, almost as a moment of grace, there was a cackle of laughter as a small five-year-old boy broke through his parents' legs, followed by another five-year-old squealing in delight, "You come back here, Sammy. We've got to go to Sunday School and learn about Jesus."

This time it wasn't a gasp but a titter of laughter and a slight reduction in the tension. Then came the voice of an embarrassed mother who worked her way free and called out to the children. "Sammy, Barry, both of you settle down. There should be no running in church." She took both of their hands, and with an embarrassed apology to those standing there, she ushered them out of the sanctuary.

Fred and Victor looked at each other, not knowing what to say. Then Victor turned towards Fran. "I should never have said that, young lady. I apologize."

"Wow, you have more guts than I figured," Fran still had her eyes fixed on him, but there was a look of growing respect. "Apology accepted, but we do need to talk more. Don't you understand that this is why many of my friends want nothing to do with the church?"

Elder Elizabeth Clifford spoke up. "I think the proper quote is, 'And a little child shall lead them. . .' Perhaps we do need to learn about Jesus in this situation."

"Maybe I shouldn't have said what I said, but he," Victor shoved a finger at Fred's chest, "has no business spouting his wrongheaded politics in this sanctuary." As he spoke, he seemed to regain some strength in his stance but with more self-control.

"Mr. Bellinger," Fran spoke, "I've heard about you. Everyone is always saying, 'He's that big rich businessman. If you want to get something done in this community, get Mr. Bellinger on your side.'"

Victor turned towards her, trying not to sound too prideful. "I just try to help where I can."

"You help," Fran continued, "but you don't listen. The Reverend here was just trying to apply the Bible to what is happening in our neighborhoods. My generation sees the church as full of a bunch of hypocrites who play with the faith but don't put it into action."

Fred stepped forward between them. "Victor, I'm not aware of you backing away from strong challenges in business negotiations. Let's you and I, and Fran," he nodded towards her, "get together and create an open conversation with the membership of this church. Maybe it's time we evaluated how faithful we are as a congregation and see if we can't focus on listening to what Jesus would say to us in this situation."

"I don't mind talking," Victor said, standing straight but leaning in, "but I don't want you to bang me over the head with all your Bible quotes. As my dear departed grandmother used to say, 'you can prove anything with the Bible.'"

"My dad used to say something like that too," said Fran. "He'd say, 'Give honkies the Bible, and they can justify anything. They just never listen to Jesus.'"

As Fred glanced at the faces, he knew that only some of them understood the term honkie. "Uh, Fran, I'm not sure . . ." Fred began.

Fran looked down and shuffled her feet. "I'm sorry, Mr. Bellinger. I shouldn't have used that word."

Victor chuckled. "I guess we both have found our tongues ahead of our brains today. That's okay, young lady. Maybe if we had some more honest conversations, we'd learn not only how to speak," his eyes twinkled, "but also how to build respect all around. You're a strong lady. I respect that."

"My name is Fran--Fran Smith--, and I think I need to explain to my daddy that God does work in mysterious ways."

Fred cleared his throat. "I think we have worshiped today, right here in the receiving line." He turned towards his young associate standing beside her husband with a look of wonder on her face. "Karen, would you lead this gathered people in prayer and a benediction."

"Uh, sure, can we all join hands and bow our heads for prayer."

"God, as you have so many times in the past, visit us with your spirit and allow us to listen, whether it be in the playfulness of little boys, the wisdom of your teenage disciples, the anger of a member, or the words of a pastor. Help our listening crack open our egos, set aside our discomfort, and sense the movement of your spirit. Even when we'd rather not, help our thoughts and actions to glorify your holy name and reflect your son who dwells among us."

Karen paused for a full thirty seconds. Some people later said it felt like ten minutes. Then she said, "If this prayer is your prayer, please say Amen."

There was a chorus of "Amens" as people raised their eyes and began to look around themselves, not totally sure what had just happened.

After the prayer, people all began to move through the door.

Some with a nod, some with a smile, others with a frown, but all realizing that a significant moment had just occurred.

Fred knew it too. He knew people would be looking to him for leadership. He just wasn't sure what those next steps should be.

"Call me," Victor said but with more calm in his voice. "I need to think about this more, but I will participate." And, turning towards Fran, "make sure it's a time when Ms. Smith can be present." He smiled, "I don't think she needs any support, but she can bring someone else if she wants."

**FOR CHAPTER RESOURCES AND ADDITIONAL CONTENT, SCAN THIS QR CODE:**
SMcCutchan.Kartra.com/page/CHAPTER1

# CHAPTER 2

# PUTTING FLESH ON SPOKEN WORDS

Elder Clifford was the last one to exit the sanctuary. She smiled as she took Fred's hand and reached out the other hand to pat him on the shoulder. "Well, my friend, I think two things have happened as a result of this worship service and your rather strong sermon."

Fred let out a long slow breath. "I'm almost afraid to ask."

"The recent incident in our city has got everyone on edge. It would help if you addressed it, but you shouldn't be surprised that not everyone will agree with you. So, the first thing I'd say is that you've hit the hornet's nest, and there will be lots of buzzing because of what you said, and the anxiety people are feeling."

"Okay, and the second thing is?" Fred raised an eyebrow, smiled slightly, and waited.

"That's hard to describe. Victor attacked you, and he was in no mood to be reasonable. He was fully prepared to use his considerable influence to punish you and maybe even get you fired."

"And?"

"AND, because of a combination of a strong-willed, insightful teenager and the intervention of some precocious five-year-old children who voiced their desire to learn about Jesus, I think, just maybe, a small miracle occurred. Instead of a church-splitting debate about your continued employment, we may have a foundation for a genuine conversation in this church about an issue tearing our society apart."

Fred stared out at the empty sanctuary. "Maybe it's just the preacher in me, but does it occur to you the biblical parallels to what just happened here? It wasn't a baby, but it was a five-year-old who uttered a truth that split our darkness; it wasn't John the Baptist, but it was a stranger who has felt the sting of being an outsider far too often that challenged us to repent or turn around and listen to a fresh word."

Elizabeth grinned and held up her hand. "I've seen that look in your eyes before – when you suddenly think you have a new idea. My afternoon is free, so I think I'll visit Lilly, assure her that you are all right, and help her process what she feels while you play with that possibility."

"I don't even agree with everything you said, Reverend. I think a church I love is in for a bumpy ride. Still, I have confidence in your integrity and," she paused and looked up at the ceiling, "your commitment to do your best to listen to God's leading. Take your time, Lilly. I will enjoy a cup of coffee together or," she paused, "if you take too long, we might even have a sip of wine and share some delicious gossip."

"Thank you, Elizabeth. I'll be sure to lock the doors and turn out the lights."

Elizabeth walked out the door with a parting wave over her shoulder as Fred began to move back to his office. As he opened the door, he heard the phone ring. He reached for the phone, made his way around his desk, and plopped in his chair. "This is Fred Livinggood. How may I help you?"

"You could start by going to Hell. If I see the opportunity, I might even help you begin the journey."

Fred felt a chill run down his spine. "I hear your anger, and I assume it's in reaction to my sermon this morning. Do you want to talk about it?"

"I don't need to talk. I listen to Jesus, not you damned hypocrites who think you know everything. It will come when you least expect it. Maybe some members of your family will pay for your blasphemies as well." Before Fred could catch his breath or form a response, the phone went dead.

He never considered himself a courageous person, but the threat to his family members sent chills of terror over his whole body. Should he call the police or just assume this was a moment of craziness from a deranged individual, and it would fade?

Well, first things first. He dialed his home, and his daughter, Bridget, answered. "Bridget, it's Dad. Let me speak to your mom."

"OK. It was an awesome sermon, Dad, and wasn't Fran the cat's pajamas? Wish I had her nerve." Then Fred heard Bridget call out, "Mom, it's Dad, for you."

Fred tried to compose himself so that he didn't convey too much alarm. When Lilly answered, he said, "Lil, is Elizabeth still there?"

"Yeah, do you want to speak to her?"

"No, but please ask her to stay until I get home. And don't let the kids go out either."

"What's wrong, Fred. Has something happened?"

"I'm sure it's nothing, Lil, but I just got a crazy, threatening phone call. I'm sure it is just someone blowing off steam, but I also don't want to put you guys at risk."

"So, someone wasn't sleeping while you were preaching," she giggled but then grew serious. "That's the problem with streaming your service over the net. You don't know who is listening. Be careful coming home, dear, and we will be fine."

As he disconnected, he thought again how grateful he was to have married Lilly Greenfield. She was three years younger than Fred and had nerves of steel when things got out of hand. He treasured her thoughts and her support "for better or for worse," as the marriage vows said.

She'd been the one who both helped him shape the sermon and gave him the courage to preach it. As he headed for his car, he thought about the events that sparked his sermon. The death of George Floyd had released a flood of protests and additional incidents around the country. Particularly troubling was the increased violence involving the police.

He would never forget a conversation he had with a Black colleague coming home from a meeting a couple of months ago. His son, Foster, was about to get his driving lesson. Fred and his colleague had been driving to a meeting together and stopped to get a sandwich on the way home. They both joked about how a juicy Big Mac and fries would necessitate an extra trip to the gym. Then, almost as an aside, he said, "Tony, I have to say I'm really getting nervous. My son, Foster, will take his driver's test this weekend. I think I'm in for some sleepless nights." He paused and then continued, "I think you told me that your son, Eric, got his license a couple of months ago. How are you and Ariel coping?"

Tony paused and set his sandwich down. He slowly wiped his mouth as if trying to decide how to respond. "You don't understand, do you?"

Realizing they had moved from gentle kidding around to a more serious conversation, Fred put his sandwich down and tilted his head slightly. "What are you talking about, Tony? Understand what?"

"We've had the talk, and we feel our stomach tighten every time he takes the car out for an event."

"I'm sorry, I don't understand."

"Look, Fred, you are a good man. I know you are compassionate and in favor of justice, equality, non-discrimination, and all those nice words that even moderates support in our society. But what you don't understand is it gets a little more personal for Black families."

"I've got the rest of the afternoon if you want to tell me more," said Fred. The sandwich wasn't as tasty now.

"Well, as a beginning, when Foster got his license, what was your family's advice to him?"

"I don't recall exactly. He'd had driver's training, and he had good reaction time. My biggest worry was that he was a little bit of a daredevil, so I guess I warned him about being careful and obeying the laws--things like that."

"Did you tell him about the ten and two positions for his hands and to be cautious about making sudden moves that might frighten a nervous police officer?"

"No," Fred fidgeted a little. "I guess that never occurred to me."

"Don't feel bad. Most white people, good white people, never have to face these issues. It's just one of many issues. Black parents have faced from day one. Many of those lessons by themselves don't seem to be that significant; put them together, and it's like a thousand little knife cuts that keep nicking at you."

"I guess that's why we call it systemic racism. It's always there but often invisible." Fred shook his head.

Tony picked up his sandwich. "You learn to live with it, but sometimes something happens that causes all those emotions you keep pressing down to suddenly boil up."

"It's not right. It's just not right. I'm not a great theologian or even a great preacher, but the church should be addressing this."

"Oh, they address it all right. Once when I was in seminary, I read a collection of sermons on race and how the Bible justifies slavery. Then they justified all the Jim Crow laws. Then segregation. But I'm not stupid. I know what preachers are up against. Most of them are afraid to disturb the peace because they want to save their jobs."

Fred grimaced. "I know I haven't been very courageous in my sermons. I just talk about loving your neighbor and the stranger, and I hope they will read between the lines."

"Don't be too hard on yourself, Fred. Most pastors, Black and White, have taken the hypocritic oath in various parts of their ministry." Tony chewed on some french fries and gazed off into the distance. "It does make you wonder at times."

"I'm sorry. What?"

Tony began to pick up his tray. "What if what the prophets said was true? Like in Micah, what if God does require that we do justice, love kindness, and walk humbly with God."

"Or," replied Fred, "Jesus really meant it when he commanded us to love our enemies and do good to those who persecute us. I've certainly got some members I could practice that on."

Tony hooted. "You're okay, Fred." He set his tray in the recycle barrel. "It is hard to learn that we are saved by grace. We certainly aren't going to be saved by how pure we are."

They left and continued their journey home. The conversation shifted to lighter subjects, but Fred could never get it out of his mind.

As issues of race and violence began to take a more prominent place in the news, Fred tried to make some allusions to the problem of justice in his sermons, but he knew that they were weak references, and it still left him feeling vaguely guilty.

**FOR CHAPTER RESOURCES AND ADDITIONAL CONTENT, SCAN THIS QR CODE:**

SMcCutchan.Kartra.com/page/CHAPTER2

# CHAPTER 3

# OUR BROTHER

The phone rang. As Fred reached for it, he noticed it was 11:30 p.m. Especially for pastors, late night calls usually meant a church member had suffered a tragedy. Fred felt his stomach tighten as he picked up the phone. He carried it to another room so that Lilly could continue to sleep. He punched the button and spoke, "This is Fred Livinggood. How can I help you?"

The voice cracked a little as she spoke. "Reverend Livinggood, this is Ariel Southgate. You don't know me, but I'm Tony Southgate's wife."

He hadn't spoken to Tony in the last couple of weeks, and it took a few moments before the synapses in his brain began to function, but then he recognized who was calling. "Yes, Mrs. Southgate. Has something happened to Tony?"

"I'm sorry to call you so late, but I just didn't know who to call. I remember Tony sharing some of your conversations and saying you were a good man."

"It's fine to call. What's happened?"

"The police picked up Eric. We've always told him to be extra careful, but he can be a little sassy." There was a pause.

Fred heard her take in a deep breath. He'd read many news accounts of black teenagers and police clashes. He could feel his stomach tighten, and a slightly sick feeling came over him. "What happened, Mrs. Southgate? Was Eric hurt?"

An edge come to her voice. "He was shot. My boy was shot by one of those cracker cops. He's at Bradley Hospital, fighting for his life."

"Where's Tony?"

"He got a call from the emergency room. One of the attendants was a friend of his. He went storming out of here in a flash. Reverend Livinggood, my husband is a good man, but he has a temper. I'm afraid of what he might do. The only thing I could think to do was call you. I thought if you were with him, being white and all, maybe they would listen to you, and you could keep him calm."

"Give me your cell phone, so I can keep in touch. I'm on my way there now." Fred started to scribble a note for Lilly, but she was standing by the door.

"What happened, Fred? Is it someone from the congregation? Was there an accident?"

"Where are my keys? I can't find my damn keys." He looked around with panic in his voice.

"Here they are, love." She held them out to him.

"It's Eric, the son of that pastor I told you about a couple of weeks ago. Eric's been shot by the police, and he is in the emergency room at Bradley." He grabbed the keys and bent to kiss Lily. "I'll call as soon as I know anything. Try to get some sleep."

"Right," she said. "I'm sure that will be easy. Fred, be careful driving."

He looked at her as he opened the door. "I know I'm really lucky," he said. "He looked at her and continued, "I know we are really lucky as a family. Two good kids, a couple of comfortable careers. And," he paused, "And we are White."

She looked a little puzzled. "I'll explain that more later," he murmured as he rushed out the door.

He'd like to believe that he was a careful driver, but Fred knew that he would be all over Foster if his son had backed out of the driveway and squealed the tires even as he was punching in his GPS for the hospital. He knew the route well, but he was also aware that sometimes he got distracted and took the wrong turn. His mind was spinning faster than a hamster exercise wheel. The thoughts kept spinning, but they didn't seem to go anywhere.

He pictured the conversation with Tony in the restaurant when he spoke about Foster getting his license and the fears Tony had about the extra risk that youth had if they were Black. He'd meant to follow up with more conversation about being Black in this country, but the demands of ministry occupied his mind, and even when they worked together, the subject never came up. For many whites, even when they talked about race and justice in mixed company, the conversation was abstract or about larger social issues. As he broke speed limits and prayed hard for green lights, Fred realized how personal and daily such matters were for people like Tony.

As he pulled into the emergency room entrance, he gave a brief snort when he recognized the advantage of being a pastor. There was a clergy parking space near the entrance. He slammed on the breaks, leaped out of the car, and sprinted towards the door. As the receptionist started to ask how he could help him, Fred spotted Tony across the waiting room. Two police officers were nearby, watching him while trying to keep a comfortable distance. As he approached Tony, he saw him rise to his full heights and march toward the officers. The officers saw him coming and began to take a defensive stance as they reached for their batons. He called out, "Tony, Ariel called me. She wants you to call her and give her an update on Eric."

Tony whirled around and stared at Fred. His face was rigid, and his eyes were flashing. Then he started to smile and chuckle at the same time. "Do you want to mention Mother Mary and Joseph as well?" Then he took three quick steps and wrapped his arms around Fred. "I was about to create a scene that would not have helped any of those you just mentioned."

"I'm so sorry, Tony. What's the latest you've heard?"

"They say he is still clinging to life, but it's very uncertain at this time."

"What can I do?"

"Get down on your knees, honkie, and pray one of your honkie prayers. I've used up all the prayers I have."

They sank to their knees, heads together, and began praying loudly. Those seated around them at first began to look away, but then an elderly woman stood and spoke. "I know all of you have loved ones you're praying for, but I heard about this on the radio when I was coming over. This man's son was shot by the police, just like you hear on the news. We need to pray for him and his son, and the police. We need a few healing miracles before this world blows apart."

Fred and Tony looked at each other and then at the people who were gathered around. Some were laying their hands on them, some prayed out loud, some collapsed, and some just bowed their heads.

Just then, a tall African American male dressed in surgical clothes burst through the emergency room doors. When he looked at the room and saw Fred and Tony on their knees in the middle, he approached. "I guess I don't have to ask who the father is," he said. "Mr. Southgate?"

Tony quickly stood up and looked with pleading eyes at the doctor.

"Mr. Southgate, I admit that a few minutes ago, I thought we had lost your son. Then, all of a sudden, he began turning around. He has a long way to go, and I can't promise what parts of the body will be compromised, but I think he's going to make it. I'll be back in about ten minutes and take you back to visit him." He placed his hand on one of Tony's shoulders. "It shouldn't have happened, but at least for now, we can be grateful that his body seems determined to live." He squeezed his shoulder, and assured him, "I'll be right back." He turned and left through the door from which he had come.

One of the policemen began to move toward Tony. Fred saw him coming and stepped between them. The officer held up his hands, moved around Fred, and began to speak to Tony. "Mr. Southgate, sir. I know you are mad as hell. I don't blame you. If it were my son, I'd be mad too, no matter who was to blame. I just want to say, sir, that

I am deeply sorry for what happened and grateful to God almighty that your son is going to live. Here is my card. When things settle down a little, and you want to talk about what happened, call me. Nothing will be served by us sticking around, so my partner and I will leave for now. Again, as a father, I am deeply sorry."

Tony looked at him but didn't make any move to respond.

The officer nodded to his partner, and they both left the emergency room.

Fred shook his head. "We may have experienced more than one miracle today."

Tony watched them leave. "At least they are still alive," he hesitated, "for the moment."

"Tony, I have no words of wisdom, but I am here for whatever we can do. Do you have a phone to call Ariel, or do you want to use mine?"

"You'd better ring her. My hands are shaking so badly I'd get the number wrong."

As Fred took out his phone, Tony continued," "Fred, you were here at a critical time. I will never forget that."

"How about you speak to Ariel, reassure her, and tell her I'm coming to pick her up while you go and visit Eric?"

**FOR CHAPTER RESOURCES AND ADDITIONAL CONTENT, SCAN THIS QR CODE:**

SMcCutchan.Kartra.com/page/CHAPTER3

# CHAPTER 4

# BE ANGRY, BUT DON'T LET THE SUN GO DOWN

The next couple of hours were a blur for Fred. He put Tony's address in his GPS and sped to his home to provide Ariel a ride. Ariel was grateful but spoke very few words to him as they drove to the hospital. He did hear her say, "I lived in terror for this night. Eric's a good boy, but he is big and strong. We fought to teach him that he had value, no matter what society said, and that he should trust that God believed in him. The sad thing is that those messages we taught him are just the qualities that some insecure police can be afraid of."

As they were pulling into the hospital parking lot, Ariel turned, "Reverend Livinggood, thank you for being here tonight. Tony was right; you are a good man."

"Please call me Fred. I'm glad I was here tonight too. But this was wrong. It should never have happened."

"You learn to live in a world that should never have happened, Fred. You're always faced with the choice."

"The choice?"

"The choice of whether God has been defeated this time or can God still work for good through those who love him."

"I'm not sure I understand. How can we see God in this?"

"You hang around Black folk much, and you'll understand that we are always searching. Otherwise, we'd end up in a massive suicide." She patted his hand as she opened the car door.

After Fred had helped Ariel find the right room and checked to see if Eric was still stable, he said goodbye and headed toward home. His mind was in a whirl, but that was the beginning of the sermon that would change his life and just a vague glimpse of a deeper understanding of his faith and God's call.

As he pulled into his driveway, the feelings of caution mixed with fear and anger gripped him. I wonder how Lil will feel about all of this, he thought. She's the realist, but she's not without a lot of courage. God, I'm thankful for her. She is a great balancing act between courage and caution.

He knew it was around 3 a.m., so he opened the door cautiously. He needn't have bothered; Lil was sitting in the living room, writing on a tablet, and fully awake. She leaped out of her chair and reached him before he had closed the door. Lil had a welcoming smile on her face, and her arms were wide open. Then she saw his face, and the smile evolved into a look of concern as she drew him into her arms.

"I'd hoped you could have gotten some sleep," he said, "but you feel like the best thing that has happened to me all day in this world."

"Before you tell me, you need to sit down, and I will get you a drink. We'll pretend it is a late evening drink rather than an early morning breakfast." She led him to the couch, gave him a brief hug and just enough shove so that he collapsed on the sofa.

He watched as Lil sashayed towards the kitchen. As she returned with a dark beer in her hand, Fred smiled for the first time in several hours. "I was so angry by the time I pulled into the driveway that I was ready to blow up the world, but now I think I'll wait until I've had this delightfully cold beer and gaze upon the vision of loveliness before me."

She stared at him for several seconds and then said, "I'm sorry for whatever evil you've experienced tonight, and I want you to tell me about it. But first, I want you to practice what you taught me several years ago when that bastard started pawing me in the grocery parking lot."

"I remember it well. That man didn't know what a tiger he'd accosted. I'll bet his genitals still hurt from where you kicked him."

"Lucky for him that his motorcycle was nearby, and he got away before you reached me, but do you remember what you told me then."

"Remind me."

"I was so furious and wanted to kill someone, but you grabbed me by my flailing arms, told me not to speak until I'd taken ten deep breaths, and let each of them out slowly. I want you to do that now."

He placed the beer down on the coaster and began to slowly take deep breaths and let them out slowly as Lilly watched him. After five breaths, he felt her sit next to him and start to rub his arms as he continued to breathe.

As he finished with the tenth breath, he heard her softly continue, "When I began to calm down, then you began your preacher talk and told me to put words around my chaos just like God had done at the creation. It worked then, and though you are far short of being God, I think you should do that now. How's that for preacher talk?" She giggled a little.

He took another long drink from his beer and set it down. He started to speak, but then his body began to shake. Lilly reached out and held him.

When he began to recover, he said, "It was horrible, Lil. They shot Eric, Tony's son. By God's grace, he is still alive, but they don't know how bad the damage is. All those words we have been using to talk about racism became very personal tonight, Lil."

"I was afraid that was what happened when you ran out of here. How are Tony and his wife holding up?"

"I think they are bouncing between gratitude that Eric's alive and fury that it happened. Tony was about to attack three cops just as I arrived."

"They weren't bad cops, Lil. Ordinary police that are caught up in a world of fear that results in evil things. That's what racism is about, Lil. We mistreat Blacks, and then we are scared to death that they'll do the same to us if they get the chance. So, out of fear, we strike out to get them before they get us."

"As you have said before about other wrongs in this world, Fred, you are not the savior; you can only do your part and trust God from there."

"It's not enough, Lil. I've said a few things but think about it. In this society, we leave the protest against evil to be made by those who are the victims. Those who benefit from society are the ones who should be objecting. We're the ones who have the power and get the benefits. What type of Christianity tolerates a world that hurts the helpless and praises a system that protects the powerful?"

"I feel a sermon coming on."

"Oh, I'll preach it, but I'm going to be far more blunt than in the past. I'm also honest enough to know that I'm also scared, Lil. I once heard a priest refer to the family as your domestic church. I can risk being fired, which I might be, but I've also got a responsibility to you and the kids."

She stood up, paced the living room a few times, and then stood directly in front of Fred. "Fredricko Livinggood."

Fred's head snapped up as if Lilly had slapped him.

"You are called by God. You are far from perfect, but the Bible has plenty of examples of God using imperfect people. I've often wondered what Sarai thought when Abram announced that God wanted them to take a journey with no guarantee of where they would end up. But they went. We'll be together, and that is what matters.

"Although," she giggled again, "if I recall, one of Abram's early acts was to try to pimp his wife to the Pharaoh to protect himself. If you even consider such an action, you won't come out of this alive."

Fred grinned. "My life is in your hands." Then he began to frown. "The truth is, none of us want to hear that we are part of the problem, but the Southgates have a right to be heard, and our congregation is going to hear it straight out."

Lilly was still standing, looking at him. "Whatever you need to say, I'll be there by your side. You don't need to worry about that. I do suggest, however, that you get some rest first. You've always said that you need to name your anger, or your anger will name you. You'll write a better sermon if you get in touch with your feelings first."

"I hate it when someone preaches my sermons back to me. You're right; maybe we both could use some bedtime."

"Men do seem to have a one-track mind at times. Might I suggest sleep first, and then we can decide what is next."

"I hate to admit it, but that sounds like a good idea." He took her hand, and they headed for the bedroom.

 **FOR CHAPTER RESOURCES AND ADDITIONAL CONTENT, SCAN THIS QR CODE:**
SMcCutchan.Kartra.com/page/CHAPTER4

# CHAPTER 5

# NOT ALL SERMONS ARE THE SAME

He had started this sermon a dozen times. His habit was to dive deeply into a biblical text, find the key elements that he wanted to get across, build some clever illustrations to explain his points, and then conclude with an invitation for the people to apply the lesson in their own lives. He always wanted to be both clear and practical at the same time. He expected people to draw their own conclusions as to how they would respond. He just wanted to stimulate them into thinking more in-depth about their faith.

This time was different. He was furious. As Lil had admonished him, this was not a good foundation for preparing a sermon. Yet every time he got too reasonable, he saw Tony in the hospital waiting room bouncing between rage and fear. The Tony he had come to know was compassionate for those who hurt and tolerant of a society that didn't understand. He knew that if it had been Foster clinging for his life, he would have been paralyzed with grief. If it were the result of someone's prejudice or ignorance, he would also have been filled with rage, especially if it was caused by someone in authority that should have known better.

For the first time, Fred became aware of something else that he had failed to understand. Not only was Eric a victim, but Tony and Ariel had bottled up both fear and anger about this very possibility for years. All parents fear for their children's safety, but typically, White parents count on society's structures to be geared towards keeping them safe. What would it be like to realize that those in power saw you and your family as a threat?

He knew his congregation members were basically good, intelligent people. They wouldn't set out to be overtly cruel or to cheat other people out of their livelihood. They would never use bigoted language and protested unfair laws and behavior. Yet, many refused to confront questions of an invisible structure in society that benefits some and harms others. It benefitted them, and they didn't want to stir the pot.

That is how he should begin his sermon. "You are all white racists, and until you understand that there is no hope for our society." Yeah, that would win him a lot of friends.

But how could he bust through their defensiveness? Every time he tried to build a logical, reasonable, calm explanation, he saw Tony shaking in terror because of a society that released people in power to hurt his family. It's not right, Fred thought, but people are too damned scared to admit it.

Maybe that's how he should begin. He could tell his own story of being awakened by his personal experience of the Southgate tragedy. As he thought about it, the voice of caution again spoke up. He didn't know any background to the shooting. What if Eric had done something to challenge the police and they had a legitimate right to act? I haven't even asked the Southgate family for permission to share their story. What right do I have to put them in the spotlight?

Damn, I'm just like everyone else. I can come up with a dozen reasons not to act. Still, regardless of what led to the shooting, it's just not right that the son you love gets shot down by the police. And it's certainly not right that a family has to live every day in fear that any action of a teenager acting like a typical rambunctious teenager can lead them to be shot by the very people who are supposed to protect us.

The phone rang, interrupting his jumbled thoughts. Almost without thinking, his hand reached out and grabbed the landline phone on his desk. "This is Pastor Livinggood. How can I help you?"

"Fred, it's Tony. I thought you might like an update on Eric."

With all of the crazy events threatening his life, Fred thought, he still takes time out to reach out to me. "Tony, I'm glad to hear your voice. What's Eric's status?"

"I guess I could say that we are lucky. The recovery is going to take a while, but it looks like Eric will make it."

"Oh God, I'm so grateful to hear that." Fred got up from his desk and started pacing as he continued the conversation. "This sounds so feeble, but is there anything that Lil or I can do for your family at this moment?"

"Well, I didn't call for this, but maybe sometime soon we can have a conversation about how Jesus would respond. I'm not in a very forgiving mode right now, but I have spent my whole adult life proclaiming a Gospel that I have trouble living."

"This may sound ridiculously small, but would you like me to have my associate preach here and have me come and fill your pulpit this Sunday? You certainly don't need that extra burden right now."

Fred heard Tony hesitate and clear his throat. "That's very kind of you, Fred, and some other time that would be good, but honestly, I don't think having a White person in our pulpit right now would be helpful. My people are pretty worked up."

Fred felt like he had been gut-punched, and yet he recognized that he had just been taught another lesson about the impact of racism. "I think I understand that, Tony. We can't act like this is just an unfortunate incident that we need to heal and move on."

"Hey, brother, I think you are beginning to understand. Thank you, I needed to hear something like that."

"Thanks, Tony, but even if it is just something small that would help you and Ariel, please let me know."

"I'll remember that. Listen, I suspect there is going to be some noise in the street over this. You may want to see if there is some way you or your members can participate. We need to demonstrate that as Christians, we can see beyond human sin and division and that we can travel together towards the Promised Land."

"I'll be there for you, Tony. Would it be all right to have Lil call Ariel and see if there are ways that she can help?"

"That would be great. Because of what you did that night, you are one of the few small lights that Ariel can see. Speaking of which, I need to go and relieve her. She hasn't left the bedside for several days. We'll check in later."

Fred placed the phone in the cradle. He looked again at the computer screen carrying the notes and ideas that he had entered as a beginning for a sermon. I may not blast them out of the water, thought Fred, but this sermon is not going to be an abstract plea to be loving to your neighbor and all be one happy family, either.

And so, the sermon that would change his life began to take shape. It started with a confession. He related some of the chapters in his personal story of his growing awareness of his participation in systemic racism. "You'll have to decide for yourself where you are on the scale of racism. It's easy for us to try to escape this reality either through denial or paralyzing guilt."

Even as he was writing the sermon, he could almost picture faces in the congregation as they listened. This point would fully focus them. Several of them would begin to be uncomfortable, and some would start to show anger on their faces.

The story of the incident that resulted in Eric's being shot and the recent street protests were all over social media. People were choosing up sides in their responses to the story. He was grateful that Tony had granted permission to share his relationship with the Southgate family.

"You can feel sad, guilty, angry, or despairing about this happening in our community. But as Christians, we don't have the liberty to ignore the pain experienced by our neighbors."

He would pause at that moment and look around at the faces of those who were listening to him. He didn't think anyone would just stand and leave at this moment, but he was sure a few would be thinking about how they could challenge him or even get him fired — justifying their efforts as "protecting the good name of the church."

He stood up and walked out of the office to check with Alice, his secretary, about his other commitments for the day. He knew he had three hospital calls to make, one counseling appointment with a couple planning their wedding, a budget committee meeting to prepare for, and some emails to respond to. He hoped that Alice hadn't received any other requests.

"That's all I know about," Alice said. Then she looked at him and paused. "Fred, you need to get some rest. Pardon me, but you look like you've been run over by a Mack Truck."

"That bad, huh?" He smiled and shook his head.

"It would be okay if you took a good hot cup of coffee and sat in the sanctuary for a while, or maybe even chuck it all and go home early."

"The question is often asked, 'Who pastors the pastor?' I can give testimony that one source is a good secretary. She is aware of what is going on, juggles difficult moments in my schedule, and occasionally offers some motherly advice."

Alice snickered. "I'll leave that up to Jill." Then some creases on her forehead appeared. "I'm aware that this racial incident is more personal than just a news bulletin, but you won't help your congregation if you don't take care of yourself. They may complain a lot, but they do care for you."

"Alice, you are a treasure. I've been lucky in marriage and secretaries. I'm thinking of taking a walk and maybe even stopping for an ice cream cone."

"Go for it."

Fred walked out the door, feeling a little better already.

As he walked down the street, he continued thinking about the sermon. It felt right to acknowledge some sins in church history but to integrate that with a reminder that, biblically, God was not defeated by our sins and patiently awaited our awakening.

He also recalled the book by Desmond Tutu and the Truth and Reconciliation Commission in South Africa. If that country could move beyond racial division and hatred, maybe there is hope for the church. He chuckled and thought, wouldn't it be ironic if the lessons on how we heal ourselves of racism came from Africa? God does have a sense of irony, he thought.

By the time he'd reached the ice cream shop, he had rationalized the excuse to have a hot fudge sundae.

 **FOR CHAPTER RESOURCES AND ADDITIONAL CONTENT, SCAN THIS QR CODE:**
SMcCutchan.Kartra.com/page/CHAPTER5

# CHAPTER 6

# THREATEN THE PASTOR

So now he had finished the sermon. And he had witnessed what turned out to be a minor miracle when Victor had confronted him at the door. Fred knew that Victor had the strength to listen to others and often gained from a vigorous debate in business negotiations. He was a powerful figure in the business world, but Fred had just witnessed a surprising moment when a teenage girl had challenged Victor. He could have dismissed Fran and seemed ready to do so, but then he suddenly took her seriously. It was a moment of grace and respect for another human.

Then, just as Fred was beginning to feel good about the possible response to the sermon, the threatening phone call occurred. He had talked to other pastoral colleagues who had had their lives threatened. Usually, they told the story after the incident was resolved, and they were able to joke with each other about the irony of preaching love and forgiveness and then having your life threatened. It was one of those pastoral experiences that were more common than the average church member knew.

It was no longer a joke. Now it was personal. Fred needed to get home and make sure his family was all right. He headed for his car. As he reached for his fob to unlock the key, Fred heard the screech of tires as a car turned the corner. This is crazy; he thought as he ducked down by his car as a shield. Things like this only happen in movies, not in real life.

Suddenly he heard the splash of eggs crashing against his car. "Stop messing around, faggot. This neighborhood belongs to the Whites. Next time you might get hurt. We protect what's ours."

Just as that car roared its motor, squealed its tires, and took off, a fiery red Jeepster Commando roared around the corner and screeched to a stop. The door opened, and to Fred's shock, Fran Smith stepped out. "Are you all right, Pastor Fred? Sorry, we didn't get here sooner. We just heard what was going down."

Fred could feel his legs shaking as he slowly got to his feet and turned to greet Fran coming towards him. "Where'd you come from? What are you doing here"?

"We heard a rumor that the bazooka gang might come and hassle you, so we thought we'd come and escort you to your home. It looks like we were a little late."

All Fred could do was stare at her. He didn't know what to say. "This isn't real," he said. "People don't go threatening a pastor because of a sermon he preaches."

"Pardon me, Pastor Fred, but this is really real. People who live in the white-white world think they are safe behind their little shields, but people of color have to face this type of shit every day. Oops, sorry, Pastor Fred. I forgot I was back in your church world."

Fred grinned and gave an open-handed gesture. A little bit of street language was not his biggest concern right now. "I've said a few crude words myself in the past few days."

"We sent another car by your house just to make sure your family was alright, but we have to be careful cruising that White neighborhood, or the police will hassle us. We sent Roger because he's pretty fair-skinned, but he still has to be pretty careful. Come on. We'll take you home."

Somewhat in a daze, but somehow knowing that Fran knew the streets far better than he did, Fred opened the car door, turned, and said to Fran, "Lead the way. I'll follow. And thanks."

"We'll get this settled down, and then we need to find a time to talk to that Victor guy."

As Fred followed the Commando, he noticed that it bore dents and scrapes indicating its hard use. It was clear that whoever owned it was more interested in its toughness than its beauty.

He was also interested in Fran's comments about taking caution while driving in different neighborhoods. It's another educational moment to be reminded that living in this community is not the same for everyone. While your honesty and purity of intent matter, for some, the impression you leave, including the color of your skin, takes precedence.

How does it shape your life to be taught by your parents or friends that when people see you walking, driving, walking into a store, or sitting on a park bench, their first impulse is to be cautious? As he followed Fran, he thought about how different teenagers might respond. He imagined some getting pleasure from seeing people's discomfort and even swaggering a little to increase the effect. He could see others becoming resentful when people always were suspicious with no justification. After repeated experience of being treated with suspicion, might others absorb the critique and think less of themselves?

The turning signal on Fran's jeep indicated that they were about to enter his neighborhood. His thoughts returned to his family and how they were reacting to these recent events. Had he placed them in danger by impulsively responding with his sermon challenging racism? It wasn't like he had advocated being a terrorist or some revolutionary act to overthrow the government. Yet, it suggested the underlying fear of change for so many in our society and the false bravado of some who think they could become heroes by fighting back.

He pulled into his driveway. He was comforted by seeing Elizabeth's car and that of her husband, Henry, as well. Whatever else was happening, he certainly was getting support from others. What was it that Jesus said right before he left his disciples in Galilee, something like "I will be with you always..."?

He waved and shouted thank you to Fran; then, he turned and opened his door.

Lilly was up out of her chair and advancing towards him, but Bridget flew into his arms before she reached him. "Daddy, I'm so proud of you."

"Glad you made it home, Tiger. Do you want a sandwich or a drink first?" Lilly said with a look that conveyed both relief and pleasure. "Elizabeth and Henry are here in the living room."

Fred gave Lilly a brief hug, and a whispered thanks into her ear.

"I think both would be great." He moved towards their living room to greet their guests. "Henry, Elizabeth, great to see you." Although Fred was not inclined to give hugs too freely, he crossed the room and took them both in his arms. "I am grateful to both of you." He looked at Elizabeth. "Bet you didn't know being an elder could be so exciting, Huh?"

Bridget came in with a plate of sandwiches, followed by Lilly with a bottle of wine and some glasses.

"Sit down, everyone. It will be good to relax a little and share some wine and talk."

"Before you say it," Elizabeth said with a glint in her eye, "this is just how the early disciples shared communion, with bread, wine, and talk."

"If I recall the story accurately," said Henry, "they also included some prayer. To give Fred some relief from his duties, allow me to gather you around and offer some prayer."

Everyone set their dishes down and gathered in a circle holding each other. Fred began, "Lord, as you led the children of Israel through the wilderness with a cloud by day and fire by night, we ask you to guide our church and our pastor and his family through our current wilderness with signs of your presence and guidance. We won't always understand, but we will strive to trust you in the journey ahead. Now, bless this food and our conversation that it might give you honor. Amen."

They gave each other a final squeeze and separated to find their seats.

"Thank you, Henry," Fred said, "Those Old Testament classes you teach at the university provide you with some powerful words of prayer."

"That was powerful this morning," said Henry. "As we have seen, the journey is not going to be easy, but we will be here for you and Lilly all the way." He turned and looked at Bridget. "That includes you and your brother, Foster, too, young lady. You'll all feel the effects of your father's ministry, and if you need support, you know where to come."

"My friends think being a preacher's kid means we have to be boring and can't have any fun. They don't know how exciting it can be when you have someone like Dad as your special pastor."

Everyone broke out in laughter.

Fred took a bite of his sandwich and chewed it with pleasure as he looked at all of them. The gouda cheese had a slightly tangy taste, and the warm ham smelled delicious. He and Lilly had often enjoyed this sandwich when they took a break during his seminary studies. She was great at knowing when he needed a break, and they would walk down the street hand in hand until they came to their favorite sandwich shop. Eating it now brought back memories of relaxing with her. She winked at him as he took another bite. He knew he was safely at home.

"You mentioned in your sermon that for White people to effectively respond to systemic racism, they must begin by facing reality," said Elizabeth. "What do you have in mind?"

"When our session offered space to Alcoholics Anonymous, I

decided I needed to look into their program a little more deeply. Do you know what's the first thing an alcoholic has to do to become a part of that program?"

"I don't know much about them, but I think the first thing is that they have to admit that they have a problem," said Henry.

"From what I have learned, there are two first steps. I don't have any clear plan, but I think, like AA, we must first confess that we have a problem and if I understand correctly, a second step is to admit that the problem is bigger than we are."

Henry chuckled, "So all our church has to do is admit they are racist and ask for God's help. Why don't you choose a difficult task to work on?"

Elizabeth spoke up, "Okay, cynic, I already witnessed one miracle, no, actually two miracles this morning. Maybe real life is more promising than all your musty old books."

Lilly clapped her hands. "I think it might be a good time to have a little wine and provide a brief sabbatical moment to allow God to devise the next miracle or so."

"Time for the healthier, younger set to separate from you alkies and go and do some homework," said Bridget as she left the room.

They looked at each other and burst out laughing. "I think we have just been chastised," said Lilly, "but maybe a little decrepit living might be appropriate for us OLD FOLKS."

For the next hour, they shared a few ideas and much laughter. Later Fred would remember this afternoon and the importance of good friends and laughter when you are under stress.

 **FOR CHAPTER RESOURCES AND ADDITIONAL CONTENT, SCAN THIS QR CODE:**
SMcCutchan.Kartra.com/page/CHAPTER6

# CHAPTER 7

# A GUILTY WALL

"You have no right to impose your political agenda on this church. I'm not a racist, and I resent the implication that I am." David Johnson had charged into Fred's office without even pausing to greet Alice, the receptionist. Fred had been filing material from last week and preparing to sort his commitments for the new week. As he turned to respond to David, he saw Alice come barging in behind him.

"David Johnson, you stop right there. You have no right barging in here like that. What if Pastor Fred was counseling someone or was deep in prayer? If someone barged into your accounting office unannounced and breathing fire, you know you would have called the police!"

The fury of her voice cut through David's anger and brought him back down to reality. "I'm not the one in the wrong here, Alice. It's that poor excuse for a pastor."

"Whether he is a poor excuse for a pastor or not, you are behaving like a spoiled brat having a temper tantrum. Now you march right back out into my office, and let's start all over, shall we?"

Fred had never seen such icy steel in his secretary. He was about to intervene when Alice stuck out her finger, pointing to the door. "Now!"

David wilted under her steely glare and began to move through the door. "Okay, maybe I was wrong, but I still want to talk to Fred, and I want to do it right now."

As Alice began to follow him out to her office, she turned and gave Fred a roll of her eyes as she said in a firm voice, "I'll be glad to check his availability."

Fred couldn't decide whether to crack up with laughter or prepare himself to hear David's complaint. Later he realized just how significant that small interruption had been. By the time David walked back into his office, both men were in better control of themselves. Fred was the first to speak, "David, I understand that you are quite upset, and I will hear you out. Let's take a moment first to thank God that Alice's intervention might allow us both to be better prepared to hear each other."

David, looking a little chagrined, nodded an assent. Fred came next to him, placed a hand on his shoulder, and began to pray, "God, this is your church, and though we have difficult things to discuss, we pray that you might visit us with your spirit and help us to listen to each other and you. Amen."

"I know you are a smart guy, Fred, but even you couldn't have planned what just happened. We're not close, but I've known Alice and her family for several years. I've never seen that steel rod in her backbone before. I think you have a fierce sentry in your outer office. May I sit down?"

Fred moved another chair around so that they were facing and indicated for David to take a seat. "I had a teenager who I barely knew intervene for me this past Sunday, and now Alice has sliced through both of our egos. I'm not smart enough to know for sure how God works, but I think we may be reassured that God is present to us."

"I'm not as religious as you are, pastor, but I think you may have a point."

"God's being present does not mean you shouldn't say what you came to say. I'm assuming that it has to do with last Sunday's sermon, but whether it does or not, I'm ready to listen. I'm also hoping when you have said what you have come to say, you will also hear my response."

"I can't say I intended to listen when I came in, but I now know I have to face Alice on the way out, so I promise you I will listen as well as speak."

They both grinned and chuckled. Then they relaxed a little.

"Tell me what you want to say," Fred extended his hand to indicate that David should begin.

"Well, it is about the sermon and the whole racial thing tearing our city and nation apart. I don't think these political things belong in the church, although I honestly don't know where they belong."

"I know you aren't accustomed to talking in these terms, and you can decline this question if you want, but I would like to hear your perspective. Not to put it too bluntly, but what do you think Jesus would want from this church right now?"

"That's more your area than mine," David said, "but I guess he would want us to be respectful of each other. I don't think Jesus would want us to rip the church apart over some political issue."

Fred nodded and was quiet for a moment. Then he said, "I'm not trying to pull the piety card on you, David, but I don't want to be the priest or scribe that passed by the wounded traveler in Jesus' parable of the Good Samaritan. I think the recent events in our city and throughout our country suggest that people are hurting in our community."

"I think that's horrible, but it is the business of the government, not the church. I never owned any slaves, and I think it was morally wrong for those who did, but that was a long time ago. We need to put that behind us and get on with life."

"What if it is not behind us yet? What if the consequences of what happened 400 years ago are still leaving a horrible scar on us as a nation? Don't you think Christ cares about what is happening to our neighbors, David?"

"I'm a down-to-earth, practical businessman, Fred. I deal with the here and now, not some future la-la land. And what's happening now is that you have a whole lot of people in this church-- good people, not some Klan-shouting bigots -- who are mighty upset with you now."

There was a light tap on his door, and Alice stuck her head in. "Since I didn't hear any volcanos erupting, I thought the two of you might want a coffee." She opened the door and carried a tray with coffee and the fixings on it.

Fred checked David's face and, seeing no creases of anger, said, "That is truly kind of you, Alice. Please place the tray on this table. We'll fix them for ourselves."

David looked up as she set the tray down and began to leave. "Alice, my mother always taught me to try to be a gentleman. I failed her and you today, and I apologize."

"That's all right, David. It is all forgotten. I'll leave the two of you to your conversation." She left, closing the door behind her.

"David, I honestly don't know what should happen next, but the combination of what I think Christ wants of us and a more recent personal experience won't let me just walk away from this. I'm meeting with Victor Bellinger soon to talk about it, and I'd be pleased to have you join that conversation."

"Bellinger! Fred, Victor is no sleazy liberal. He'll whip your ass and hang you out to dry."

"Normally, I might agree with you, David, and he started that way Sunday. Then his version of Alice intervened, and he also made a 180-degree turn and agreed to talk further. I think that if he, you, and several elders could agree with me on what to do next, we might discover some new possibilities."

David reached into his suit pocket and extracted a long envelope. "Just so you know what you are dealing with, Fred, this is a petition signed by half of your elders and fifty more people. They would like you to save the church a lot of embarrassment and resign quietly. I'm not sure they would be open to any next steps, but if Victor and I step in, we could convince them to give you another month to present your case."

**FOR CHAPTER RESOURCES AND ADDITIONAL CONTENT, SCAN THIS QR CODE:**

SMcCutchan.Kartra.com/page/CHAPTER7

# CHAPTER 8

# LILLY

Being a pastor's wife is not an easy task. There are a few advantages and some significant disadvantages. Lilly thought about both as she sipped her third cup of coffee on Monday morning. She hadn't slept well last night but had tried to be as quiet as possible so Fred could get some much-needed sleep.

The past week had been a strange and exhausting week. The build-up to Fred's sermon was one of those invisible tasks for a pastor's spouse that few people could imagine. When Fred returned from being with Tony and Ariel at the hospital, she could see the cascading emotions coursing through his eyes and face.

She flashed back about twenty-two years to when she had first met Fred Livinggood. He had stumbled into the Emergency Room where she worked with a seriously bruised face, holding his arm and showing significant pain on his face. She often gave thanks that she had been on duty during that ice storm and just coming off treating a patient when he came through the door. Her last patient had coded, been revived, and then rushed to surgery. Her emotions were raw, and somehow having a patient with apparent problems that she could treat and who was rather shy lifted her spirits. Even now, she was slightly embarrassed that she violated the rules and slipped her business card into his pocket with the penned message, "just in case you might want more information on your treatment."

A week later, she was pleased that he called her and invited her out to dinner. Again, she recalled his somewhat hesitant invitation with delight, combined with saying he understood if she were too busy. While it got him into trouble at times, he was always putting others first. One of the roles she assumed in their marriage was raising flags of caution when she saw he was carrying it too far.

Wrestling with when she should speak up and when she should just be of support was always a concern. Who knew that being a pastor's wife meant you also had to be a theologian in residence? Of course, when they courted and eventually married, she didn't even know what those words meant, but wrestling with such questions was the beginning of a marvelous spiritual journey. Fred was often cautious about being too bold theologically with the congregation, but privately he taught her not to be afraid of her doubts or having concerns about offending God. He carried a passion for integrity into his ministry and both his and their spiritual journey.

She thought about that as she sipped her coffee. She knew the Southgate tragedy had shaken him. He had wrestled with what to say to the congregation about the issue of racism all week. He'd always been for fairness and against all forms of racism and bigotry. Yet, with Eric's shooting, the topic moved from being a debatable conversation to either have or avoid to being deeply personal. He'd received pushback before when he tried to preach about issues, but it was always trying to comfort the afflicted or at least those who were bothered. Now he was willing to afflict the comfortable and proclaim the living out of a gospel in which he sincerely believed.

And what was the wife's role in such a situation? She agreed with him on the evils of racism, but that had been from the comfort of a safe marriage and a stable lifestyle. In her nursing career, she worked with many Black nurses and doctors and always showed them the respect she expected everyone to have. Yet, she admitted that she had never truly appreciated the pressures many of them lived with daily in our society. As always, when challenged in life, she knew that she had lots to learn.

She had heard from some of the women in the congregation about peoples' upset regarding the sermon. Some of them had been quite direct. This was another feature of being a pastor's spouse. Somehow, she was supposed to restrain her husband but do it quietly so the congregation wouldn't get too upset. Besides, she knew that Fred had received a flood of emails and over a dozen calls challenging him and threatening to get him fired if he didn't withdraw from the issue.

Fred came out of the bedroom, already dressed. He gave her a brief hug and a kiss and then left for work. She watched him pull out of the driveway.

She refilled her cup and sat back down.

"Damn those people. Don't they realize they're hurting my husband when all he's doing is trying to save their asses or souls? They can all go to Hell for all I care." She was shouting and pounding on the table at the same time. She was comforted that the house was empty. Fred had counseled her that God had heard far worse things than she could dream up, and it was far more critical to be honest with God than to be polite. *I hope he's right, or I could be in big trouble.*

Still, she was somewhat embarrassed at her outburst. Maybe not with Fred's compassion, but she did care for the people in the congregation. How could they be so nice one moment and so mean-spirited the next? She guessed that "Forgive us our debts as we forgive our debtors" had become a new challenge for her. She hoped that God did understand.

That was another challenge of being a pastor's wife. She was supposed to act with decorum and have an unshakable faith even when others had their knives out with her husband as a convenient target. *If they are lucky, they'll never find out how fierce I can be.* Once you have to intubate people who are in a panic mode and even see small children die as you work on them, you develop an ability to make decisions and act with determination without worrying about how you may appear to others. She recalled a couple of doctors who discovered that lesson to their surprise as they worked at her side.

Still, as she sat there, she began to think about how she would be able to support Fred and her family. She knew Fred would be worrying about how this would affect his family. He needed to know that if things got rough, his family would get all the support they needed. The family held plenty of discussions about what it was like to be a pastor's family, and they, too, had developed a capacity to see beyond the immediate and stand up for what needed to be done.

Even before the infamous sermon, she knew Fred wrestled with three forces. First, he worried about his family if this resulted in losing his job. Second, he worried about how it would affect the members of the congregation that he dearly loved. And third, he wrestled with his integrity as a person and pastor. Even though she was scared when she said it, Lilly was glad that she found the courage to reassure him that she would be with him whatever he decided to do.

Now, however, she had to help him decide his next steps. The thing about being a pastor is that no matter what happened last Sunday, the following Sunday you had to stand before the people and speak again. Should he keep pushing, or should he give the people a breather and shift to a kinder subject? She chuckled as she thought about a brief moment a few years ago when it was all the rage to wear bracelets and wrist bands bearing the acronym WWJD (What Would Jesus Do?). As Fred would often kid in private, what they often forget is that what Jesus did got him killed. Still, it was a legitimate question, maybe altered a little to <u>What would Jesus have the church do?</u> And what should a pastor do if the church resisted?

Without forcing any particular style of prayer, Fred had taught her a lot about prayer. She was reasonably sure she would learn much more about prayer in the next few months. She recalled a particular sermon that Fred had preached sometime in the past based on a Scripture passage that said, "In everything, God works for good with those who love him and are called according to God's purpose," or something like that. What she remembered from the sermon was the assertion that there is nothing that happens in which

God wouldn't be present and at work, no matter how good or bad things were. Even though she admitted she was scared, she hoped some good would come out of this.

Okay, three cups of coffee are enough for now. She was on call at three this afternoon, and another task was to get the house straightened up so that when Fred came home, he could focus on other things.

**FOR CHAPTER RESOURCES AND ADDITIONAL CONTENT, SCAN THIS QR CODE:**

SMcCutchan.Kartra.com/page/CHAPTER8

# CHAPTER 9

# ESCÚCHEME

The first thing Fred saw as he drove into the church parking lot was a crude sign painted on the side of the church. WHITES ARISE, DEFEND GOD'S CHURCH AGAINST

MONGREL INVADERS.

It was sloppy, obviously painted in the middle of the night. Okay, I guess that determines my first agenda item. I must call the police and report some vandalism. Unfortunately, once they get here, that will occupy a good portion of the morning.

As he walked towards the church office entrance, he noticed a much smaller message just to the left of the larger one and in a different color of paint. It was almost plaintive in its simple message: "escúcheme."

Had someone walked by during the night and seen the larger sign? This smaller one was in Spanish, so was it a recent immigrant crying out for help but from the shadows? While racism was the immediate source of conflict for his church, Fred knew racism could quickly bleed over into all sorts of fears generated in the hearts of those who sense their dominant place in this society slipping away.

The thought occurred to him as he stuck his key in the lock and prepared to open the door that Escúcheme or "Listen to me," might not be a bad motto for what needed to happen in his church and the world. I wonder how many languages I can write that in?

Alice was already at her desk, focused on her computer screen as he came in. "Only about 2,000 messages waiting for your immediate and personal response," she quipped. "I've separated them into two piles. There are a hundred or so that think you walk on water, but the rest are some version or other suggesting how far you should sink."

"Alice, I'm afraid I'm having a bad effect on you. I'm told that before I came, you were the efficient but soft-hearted center of all church gossip and quickly able to tamp out any fire that threatened to erupt."

"Ha! That was before Gene died and left me all that money to spend. I'm free at last. Look out world; God has set me free to be the guardian of God's holy temple!"

Fred broke out in a wide grin and deep chuckle. "I think David got a taste of that the other day. Maybe I should just turn over that larger pile of messages on my desk and let you take care of them."

She turned to face him. "I'd be delighted to do that, but maybe you should glance at them first so that you know the temperature of the water."

"I'll do that, but first, we need to call the police and report some vandalism on our wall out there. Some artists chose to become a channel for creative complaint."

"Oh, my goodness. I came in through the side. What did they do?" A worried look spread across her face as she reached for the phone.

"There were two of them. The larger one wants to call out the troops and defend the sacred cause of the White race. The second one is much smaller and poignant. It's almost a silent scream. All it says is escúcheme or listen to me."

"My husband used to defend many people who simply wanted someone to listen to them. The world would be better if we could just learn to do that."

"Alice, do you read minds too? That was just what I was thinking when I came in through the door."

"Well, there aren't two thousand messages, but there are probably fifty messages that you can practice on in there. "Que Dios te bendiga."

"You are full of surprises. Now you are a linguist as well." He shook his head as he headed toward his office. "Thank you, Alice. I'm beginning to think that it is the women in this world that will save it."

"Glad you are catching on, Padre."

Still grinning, Fred reached for the pile of messages placed neatly on his desk with post-it notes on each stack. One said, "Walk on water." A second said, "Try treading water." A third said, "Sinking fast--reach for the nearest ring buoy."

He decided to begin with the "Walk on Water" pile to build up his confidence. But first, he thought, I will use the Keurig to make a strong coffee cup to fortify myself.

While waiting for the coffee to fill his cup, he pulled out a large piece of newsprint and began to identify extra spaces for the notes and how to respond. The first circle said, "thanks for the support."

The second said, "Creative possibility for dialog." A third said, "I hear your anger and would like to talk further." A fourth said, "Wait five days and respond gently." A fifth said, "Personal attack. Name it, but don't respond in kind."

He knew there would be others, but this would help him organize his responses. He hated conflict. In the past, he had leaned too much on his innate desire to be a people-pleaser. He uttered a brief prayer that he would discover a creative way to help the church grow in their ability to permit the Spirit to give birth to new possibilities.

An hour later, the police arrived. He considered it a blessing that he had to interrupt his task and talk to them about the vandalism. Interestingly, one of the two officers that greeted him was African American, and the other was Caucasian. This will be interesting to see how each of them responds, he thought.

A half-hour later, he recognized that the two officers used humor to pierce any tension that might arrive between them. Also, they were careful to use professional behavior to establish their relationship with Fred until they could ascertain where he was on the scale of social sensitivity.

"Do you like to be addressed as Father, Pastor, Reverend, or what?" Officer Glazer asked.

"Reverend or pastor will be fine, although I'm not too concerned about titles. My first name is Fred."

"Well, Reverend Fred, it is clear that we have what I hope is a small incidence of vandalism that reflects the larger issue of racial unrest. There is a lot of that in this city but also all over our society."

Officer Delgado chimed in, "But what is this small sentence off to the left?"

Fred responded, "It's Spanish. Escúcheme means listen to me."

"Man, if I had a nickel for every time that would lower the temperature in a situation, I'd be rich," Delgado said with a weary smile.

Officer Glazer continued. "Since we don't know who did this, we'll file a report and maybe keep watch on this area for a few days to see if they return. Is there anything particular that your church is doing that might have stirred this up?"

"We're trying to understand and respond to the issue of racism in our society."

"Good luck with that," Glazer said with a smile. "Somebody must think you are messing with reality, and that threatens them."

"This may be difficult for you officers to discuss, but it got a little more personal when recently the child of one of our neighboring churches was shot in a police incident. It's stirred up some fairly deep feelings."

Glazer glanced at Delgado and uttered a brief, "The Southgate incident, I'm assuming."

When Fred nodded, Delgado continued, "That's stirred up a lot of people, but how is a White church like this one," he glanced at the church building, "getting involved?"

"Your job is to protect people when things go wrong, and our job is to heal the wounds and give all people hope. Neither of us does it perfectly, but we can't stop trying."

"So, where do you start?" Glazer asked. His look suggested that he wanted to know.

"I'm not sure, but our little sign-maker may have given us a clue. We've got to help people to listen to each other. I don't see much of that going on right now."

"That's a righteous goal, reverend," said Delgado. He reached into his pocket and grabbed a business card. "If I can help, please let me know."

A thought occurred to Fred, and he said, "Thanks, officer, I may just take you up on that."

"Sure, why not?" Glazer said and also handed him a card. These police/civilian incidents give us all a..." He chuckled and continued, "...I was going to say it gives us all a black eye, but maybe that is not the right way to say it."

Delgado grinned and said, "Yeah, Phil, you better watch your language. According to the big sign, we might be taking over. Maybe then we'll all have purple eyes."

"And we'll all be zebras." He turned back to Fred, winked, and said, "In the meantime, we'll file a report and be back in touch if we have additional questions."

As the police car pulled away, Fred thought, "Once again, God, you may have opened a connection that might prove useful as we proceed."

Just then, his associate drove up and parked near him. "I know that look," she said as she greeted him. "Some other crazy idea has just popped into your head."

"Do you know the term 'thin moment'?"

"I think I read about it in seminary. It's part of Celtic spirituality, isn't it? That moment when God breaks through our finite reality with a larger or fresher truth."

"Very good, Karen. And in the last few weeks, I think I've experienced several thin moments when God has broken into my reality with fresh possibilities."

Karen's eyes lit up, and she grinned. "I bet I remember one of them. Who would have guessed that two rambunctious five-year-olds could have interrupted that clash at the church door and offered us a win-win possibility instead of a win-loss one?"

"That was certainly one of them." Fred turned and pointed to the graffiti on the church wall. "And maybe that small sign below the larger one can be another."

"Escúcheme," Karen said slowly, having difficulty pronouncing it. "I don't speak Spanish. What's it mean?"

"Probably one of the universal prayers of our world, but one that few pay attention to. I'm not good at Spanish either, but if I remember correctly from my college class, it is the imperative form roughly translated 'Listen to me.'"

"Imperative form?" Karen drew closer to the sign and examined it more closely.

"It's the command form of the verb. Roughly it is saying, 'You need to listen to me.'"

"I guess everyone wants that," Karen said.

"What if it became a plural statement to our church. If we are truly going to build a Christian community, to love our neighbor as Christ commands, then we must first learn to listen to each other."

"It would sure save a lot of marriages. Who knows? If I could get Ezekiel to listen, I might even be able to get him to understand a thing or two." Karen held up her hands with palms facing out. "I'm sorry, Zeke and I had a fight before I left, and I'm still a little rattled. The truth is, I need to listen more too."

Fred reached out, placed a hand on her shoulder, and smiled. "I've watched you two before. You are both strong-willed, but your love is deep. You will get through this. Maybe Zeke will follow his namesake and command the valley of dry bones to come to life."

"Ever the optimist," Karen said with a twinkle in her eyes. "But you're right. It was a silly argument anyway. But maybe I should be Mrs. Ezekiel and give him a call."

She grabbed her phone from her purse, turned, and began to walk away. "I'll be right back."

Fred walked towards the office door, glancing at the graffiti, and speaking as he went, "Thank you, my little graffiti artist. You may have provided me a glimpse of a creative possibility."

**FOR CHAPTER RESOURCES AND ADDITIONAL CONTENT, SCAN THIS QR CODE:**
SMcCutchan.Kartra.com/page/CHAPTER9

# CHAPTER 10

# THE SEEDS OF A PLAN

"What did the police have to say?" Alice asked as he came into her office.

"Concerning the graffiti, there isn't much they can do but file a report. However, they may have planted a seed about how I should respond to all those notes on my desk."

"Oh, goody, are you going to have all of them arrested?"

"You really are on your game today, Alice. The truth is, I will invite them to listen to each other and to the Holy Spirit speaking to this church. Don't publish the bulletin as I gave it to you. I'm going to make some changes."

"I've watched this happen before. I never print it until at least Thursday."

"You're the best, Alice."

Fred walked into his office, closed the door, and looked at the several piles of notes spread on the card table he had set up in one corner of the room.

He pressed the intercom and said, "Alice, when Karen returns, ask her, when she has a moment, to join me here."

He thought about what had happened in the last several weeks. He had to admit that he was reluctant to speak too openly of the several incidents as "thin moments" or "God moments" because it sounded almost magical or superstitious. He had watched and spoken disdainfully of several prominent religious figures who claimed to definitely know that God had spoken to them or that the Holy Spirit guided them. They left the impression that if you challenged them, you were also challenging God.

As he mused further, he recognized that he wanted to invite all the members to practice assuming that, as they deeply listened to each other, -- especially those who held differing ideas, they mighse God's Spirit among them. Another playful thought popped up. He wondered if, at that first Pentecost experience, Christ's followers had not only heard God speak through languages different from their own but also through people whose opinions differed from their own as well? That could get crazy and maybe even frightening. No wonder many tried to escape the experience by suggesting that people had had too much wine to drink.

He was still playing with the idea and considering how it might be worked into a sermon when he heard a soft rap on his door. "Come in, Karen. Be careful where you step. I've got papers everywhere."

Karen carefully stepped through the door. Fred noticed a slight glow on her face and a satisfied smile. "I think 'Them Bones, Them Bones, Them Dry Bones' will become my favorite spiritual from now on."

Fred laughed softly. "I assume your phone call with Zeke went well?"

"Better than well. When you concentrate on listening deeply to another person, you can hear all sorts of things, including an invitation to a delicious dinner out tonight. Woo Hoo! I owe you, Fred. Alice said you wanted to talk."

"First, I'm glad the search committee had the wisdom to call you as my Associate." Before Karen could begin to respond, Fred interrupted. "No, don't say anything. You'd try to dismiss it out of embarrassment. Just accept it as true.

"And second, I thought that was a beautiful prayer that you closed with in our reception-line worship moment on Sunday.

"And third, but maybe more difficult, I want you to help me think through our next steps in this process."

Karen glanced around at the piles of notes and was amused at some of Alice's titles for some of the piles on the card table. "You may not walk on water, but that was a powerful and courageous sermon on Sunday. I, too, am blessed to be on your staff. Where do you want to begin?"

Fred shifted some papers off a chair and indicated that Karen take a seat. "Have you ever thought about the Pentecost experience in Acts? How at least part of it can be understood as an experience of truly diverse people who spoke in differing languages, and perhaps differing perspectives about the world, discovering that they could allow the Spirit to enable them to understand each other?"

"Sounds exciting. We certainly have a diverse world and, to a lesser degree, various thoughts in this congregation. Some people speak of Pentecost as the birthday of the church. Do you think we might be on the brink of something new here?"

"Just beginning to consider that possibility, though I don't know where that leads us. I don't want to go off in some cult-like direction. Whatever we do should be grounded in the real world that God has given us."

"Shucks, that means we can't go and get drunk on good wine at nine in the morning like the early disciples were accused of doing."

Fred realized that his body was pretty tense, and he burst out laughing as he shook his head at Karen's acerbic humor. "The four women in my life have certainly blessed me."

"So which pile is first?" Karen asked with a smile.

"Let's brainstorm for a time but keep an eye on the clock so you have plenty of time to get ready for your dinner date with Ezekiel. And," Fred reached in his wallet, "I'll be asking a lot of you in the next year or so, so allow me to provide you and Zeke with a little extra so that you can make tonight extra special." He slipped a few bills from his wallet and handed them to her.

She started to resist, and he gave her a look that quickly convinced her best response was to accept the gift graciously. "Okay, thank you very much. We'll also celebrate you and Lilly tonight."

"You saw the little sign that said Escúcheme? When I translated that for the police officers, Delgado, the African American one, quipped something like, 'If I had a nickel for every time people just listening to each other could lower the temper of a situation, I'd be rich.' It got me thinking about what might happen in this congregation if we could build a foundation for our members to do just that. Regardless of our differing opinions, everybody would listen to each other deeply and expect God could speak something new just through that."

"Wow! If we could pull that off even in this congregation, think about what Good News we would have to offer the world around us."

"So, I was thinking; you are rather good with the information technology. Could we design some ways that we could invite all the members to practice listening to each other?"

"You mean like using Zoom or something like that?"

"Yeah, something like that, but let's get creative in how we do that if we could start with each person responding to something easy and compiling it as a way to build a composite picture of how God might be speaking to us at this time.

"Maybe," Fred continued, "we could begin with the assumption that God has invited us to be part of this congregation for a reason. Then, we invite them to tell us in a few sentences what caused them to be a part of this congregation."

"I think that could build a fascinating picture of our church, but won't they want to know when we will get to the racism part that started all of this?"

"Probably so. I just don't want to begin with an argument about who is right or wrong. I also want to bring Victor, David Johnson, Fran, and maybe a couple of others into this planning so that it feels like we are working together. Sort of a demonstration of the type of sharing we are inviting them to participate in."

"I'll research how best to set this up, and you can set up a meeting with Fran and Victor. She's a fascinating character. Where did you find her?"

"I think one of the boys in the youth group brought her to one of the meetings, and she just kept coming. Though I think the Sunday of the infamous sermon was one of the first times she had been to worship. I haven't talked to her much, but I get the impression that she's been one of those 'spiritual but not religious' types. She has a hunger for a greater truth but hasn't been into church life much in the past."

"Fred, you keep coming up with these accidental encounters, and you will make a believer out of me yet."

"As Lilly keeps saying about you, Karen, some people can say the words but have problems walking the walk, whereas you seem to be able to walk the walk while you still struggle with the talk."

"Ever since seminary, I've been haunted with the question of what if the Bible were true? What if God does expect us to do justice, love mercy, and walk humbly with God? Or what if we took Jesus seriously in the church and tried to forgive every member seventy times seven times? That would be a whole lot of forgiving. I remember those Amish people a few years ago who astounded the world when they offered forgiveness to those who shot their children. What if all those things are true, and we are just fooling ourselves when we try to find loopholes to justify our lives?"

"What if the Bible were true, huh? That'd be a scary thought." Fred shook his head and raised an eyebrow. "Do you suppose God might start a revolution of learning how to love each other in the church?"

"Now, who is being the cynic?" quizzed Karen with a chuckle. "I'll work on the tech part, and you can develop a plan to help us learn to love each other." As she left his office and saw Alice working at her desk, she said, "You better watch out, Alice. Your boss is beginning to think about radical ideas."

"I know. First, he thinks that the races should be equal, and then he takes women seriously. One does wonder if these are the signs of the second coming."

 **FOR CHAPTER RESOURCES AND ADDITIONAL CONTENT, SCAN THIS QR CODE:**
SMcCutchan.Kartra.com/page/CHAPTER10

# CHAPTER 11

# CHURCH BUSINESS
# AND PEACEMAKING

Fred realized that he had no idea how to contact Fran. She wasn't a church member and only started attending the youth group a few months ago. He decided that Bridget might be his best source, so he waited until she would be on her lunch break at school and called her on her cell phone. As he punched in her number, he marveled at how the world of communication had changed.

It took about four rings before he saw her smiling face on his phone. "Hi, Dad, what's up?"

"Bridget, I wondered if you knew how I might get Fran's contact information?"

He saw her turn her head and heard her call out. "Heh, Samantha, come over here; I've got a question for you."

Fred could see a series of dining tables at which numerous youth were eating and talking. At one of the tables, a tall redheaded girl stood up and signaled with her hand that she was coming over.

Bridget turned back to the phone. "My friend, Samantha, will know. It's so loud in here that we'll probably have to step out into the hall."

"Sam, this is my father, and he wants to get in touch with Fran. You got her number?"

"Yeah, I think so. She'll probably be over in the science lab now

-- unless, of course, she's out organizing some protest or other. Our gal Fran doesn't waste any time. Here it is." As Samantha read off the number, Bridget repeated it to her dad over the phone.

Fred decided to wait until after school let out to place his call. She answered on the third ring. "This is Fran. Black Lives Matter, and I have your back. What can I do for you?"

"Fran, this is Pastor Fred Livinggood. I wanted to see if you are still interested and willing to meet with Victor Bellinger and me to discuss some possible next steps here at the church."

"Sure, Pastor Fred. What have you got in mind and when?"

"I haven't talked to Victor yet, but I was thinking sometime early next week if you both were available."

"I'm available Thursday and Friday after school or anytime Saturday. Would we meet at the church?"

"I'll have to check all that with Victor first, and then I will get back in touch with you. By the way, as Victor suggested, you can bring someone else along with you."

"So, if we were in the movies, at this point, I'd ask if I need to have my lawyer with me."

Fred chuckled, "I don't think that will be necessary, but you can consider whether there is a friend you'd like to bring that also has good ideas."

"Yeah, I got that, but what are we talking about? Is he still upset about your sermon, or are we talking about how Whites get more breaks than we do, or what?"

"I can't guarantee where we will go, but I hope we will begin by thinking about how our church can learn to have difficult conversations with each other and still show respect for each other."

"Will it just be a bunch of adults, or will young people like me be able to participate?"

"Jesus once said that a little child will lead them, and if you recall, in that confrontation on Sunday, it was a couple of five-year-olds that broke the tension. So, who knows where we will end up? But I think the interaction among Victor, you, me, and a couple of others could give birth to some creative possibilities."

"That's almost scary for me, Pastor Fred. I know how to lead protests, confront the police, and challenge authorities, but listening to, and being listened to, by some bigwig adults is new territory for me."

"Sadly, it's new territory for many of us, but I promise you I'll have your back, and we will treat others with respect and see what God can do among us."

There was a moment of silence, and then Fran said, "I like and respect you, Pastor Fred, but I don't have much experience with that faith business. Not sure I'd be very good at it. I don't want to offend you, but I don't even know if God exists, let alone how God operates in this world."

"Being that honest about your beliefs and doubts is the first step, and I am confident you will do fine. And thank you for trusting me, Fran. I'll be in touch."

Fred wasn't sure, but he thought he heard a little crack in Fran's voice as she said goodbye and hung up.

Now he needed to follow through with Victor, and perhaps David Johnson, and see if they could respond with as much honesty and integrity as Fran had shown.

\*\*\*\*\*\*\*\*\*\*\*\*\*\*

Alice called Victor, alerted Fred when they had connected, and switched Victor over to Fred's line.

"Victor, as we agreed, I'm calling to set up a time when we can have some further conversation about how we are to proceed as a church in these volatile times."

"I think you've talked to David Johnson. I think he would like to be included in these planning conversations. And of course, that young lady, what was her name--Francis, Fran, something like that."

"Yes, I've talked to her, and she has agreed and given me some times when we might get together. Her suggestion was after school on Thursday or Friday or anytime on Saturday next week. Once we've agreed, either you or I can call and invite David."

In looking at my calendar, Friday afternoon would work. I assume this first meeting will only be a couple of hours --getting to know each other, setting some objectives, things like that. What time does school let out?"

"I think she can be available any time after about 3:30, maybe even a little earlier, depending on where we meet."

"That's fine. Do you want to use our conference room? It's on the fifth floor and has a great view."

Fred smiled. "You think that might protect you from being hit over the head with a Bible."

Victor barked a loud laugh. "Sorry about that, pastor. That's another time when my tongue got ahead of my brain." There was a brief pause, and then Victor continued, "To quote another participant at that conversation, 'We honkies are like that.'" Then while continuing to chuckle, he said, "I like that young woman. She's got some steel in her backbone. I don't know how we will handle the church issue, but I think I will enjoy having her as part of the conversation."

"Victor, you and I may disagree on several things, but I've always admired your ability to both say what you are thinking and to listen to others when they disagree."

"Okay, I'll schedule the conference room and call David, and I'll count on you talking to Fran. We started off heavy, so assure her I'll be on my best behavior."

As Fred disconnected the phone, he felt some tension release from his shoulders. He was a realist and knew there would be some rough times ahead, but he also felt there was at least a possibility that something fresh could develop.

He picked up the phone. It rang a few times, and then he heard her voice, "This is Lilly Livinggood. To whom do I have the pleasure of speaking?"

"You are speaking to your loving husband, who would like to invite you to dinner at the restaurant of your choice this evening."

Well, loving husband, your timing is perfect. I've just finished a phone call with a member of your loving congregation who felt obligated to share with me, in complete confidence, that you are a total idiot and a complete slave to the company line – translated, that is, to the national Presbyterian church. And, as an act of kindness, they felt it was important to tell me that if I don't straighten you out, a group of faithful members are organizing to get you fired. So, let's pick a restaurant that offers a fine wine which we can use to toast these wonderful members."

"I'm so sorry, Lil, that you must endure this. I think I have some news that will counterbalance that, but I will pick you up at about six."

"Don't fret about this, Fred. I may not have known what I was getting into by marrying a pastor, but I've never regretted it. Love you. See you at six."

Sometimes it's the little things that give you courage, thought Fred. Those last few words that Lilly spoke filled Fred with new energy.

Ideas were beginning to form in his head about what should be the focus of next Sunday's sermon. He usually liked to work from the Scripture to the message, but this time he admitted to himself, that the sermon will be a message in search of a supporting Scripture.

**FOR CHAPTER RESOURCES
AND ADDITIONAL CONTENT,
SCAN THIS QR CODE:**
SMcCutchan.Kartra.com/page/CHAPTER11

# CHAPTER 12

# LIVING WITH GUILT

Fred picked Fran up from her school. He was a little surprised and pleased that she had chosen to dress up for the occasion. "Just put your backpack in the back seat. I can run you home after the meeting, so you can just leave them there."

Fran shoved the backpack in the back seat, took her purse, and climbed into the car. She extracted a comb and ran it through her hair. "Thanks, Pastor Fred. I'm a little nervous about this meeting. It's easier to plan for a protest march or a sit-in than to meet adult standards and try to discover a way to help people talk about things that frighten them."

"First, you will do fine. I recognize that you made a special effort to present yourself as an adult in a business meeting."

"I told a couple of adults I trust about this meeting. One of their suggestions was I should not provide them with any extraneous excuse not to listen. I should dress like they expect and speak in White person language. It might even confuse them into listening to us."

Fred looked at her in amazement. "If they are willing, I wouldn't mind talking to your two friends. I'm aware that survival in this society requires that Black people know White people better than the reverse, and if this develops as I'd like, I could benefit from some of their wisdom."

"I'll talk to them, but what do you think will happen in this first meeting?"

"While I don't think they would admit to being frightened, they are uncomfortable about the impact on the church of becoming involved with what they see as a volatile and often divisive subject. The church members are comfortable with each other, and my church even likes being poked a little about uncomfortable topics but suggesting major change can frighten them."

"So, what's your idea? That sermon you preached was pretty pushy. Are you going to give it to them again next Sunday? I like to see people squirm a little when it comes to injustice. Our society needs to face reality, or things can get really bad. I don't know much about it, but Christian folks are supposed to be good, aren't they?"

Fred paused for a red light and looked around at the people on the street and in the other cars. "See those people out there —- Black, white, Asian, and lots of others. Most of them just want to live and be happy and and productive. Until they are challenged, most of them are thinking, 'You don't bother me, and I won't bother you.'

"In a sense, most churches are just a little picture of society as a whole with the exception that they think they are connected to a God that wants them to strive to be better. The larger message of a church is that you can be even better and happier if you are part of a community of people who practice a love of others that releases everyone to be better."

"That's pretty cool, but I don't get the impression that a lot of churches are like that. The word on the street is that churches are pretty selfish and good at protecting what they have while blaming others for being really bad."

"Ouch, that is probably pretty close to being true, but it isn't what we believe God wants from us."

"You are saying the church doesn't listen to their own God?"

"Double ouch, but there is another factor that leads to where I hope we will begin to explore in this meeting. In church or out of church, most people know they are not as good as God would want them to be. Most people handle that guilt by hiding their failures and pretending that they are better than they are. And they can get defensive when someone points out their lesser qualities."

"Oh, yeah, I get it." Fran begins to get excited and bounces a little in her seat. "That's why White people get so angry when you tell them they are racist. They like to see themselves as good people and blame the problem on others. While it doesn't solve the problem, and it doesn't excuse the injustice, sometimes we like to blame White society for all our problems, when sometimes we don't do so well ourselves."

"I think you have glimpsed part of the problem. In the Bible, Paul says, 'I do not do what I want, but I do the very thing I hate.'"

"Yikes, that is so true. How many times do I do the very thing I know is wrong? And I get angry at someone who points that out because I want to pretend I'm better than I am. That's deep, Pastor Fred. The main difference between the White race and other races is that they have more power and can get away with it."

"I'm afraid you are right. And if you have learned to benefit from that, it is doubly hard to have that pointed out and be asked to give up the advantage."

"Is that what we are talking about at this meeting -- how to get people to deal with their guilt and give up some of their advantages?"

"That's part of it." Fred turned into a parking lot of a large building. "Here is where Victor works, and he has offered us to use his conference room on the fifth floor."

Fran gazed at the building. "Wow, that is a snazzy building. No wonder he doesn't want to give it up."

"Wait till you see the conference room," Fred said as he held the door for her to enter the building. "Fran, before we go in, I want to say a couple of things. While I appreciate you're trying to 'fit in,' I don't want you to feel pressed to sacrifice your integrity. While you will gain from listening to them, remember that they can also gain from listening to you. You are bright and alert. Don't deny them the benefit from hearing you."

"I told papa you were an unusual man. Thank you for saying that."

"One other thing. It is okay to disagree with me or challenge something I say. I need your insight, even if it is different from mine."

"You got it, boss. Kowtowing ends as we enter this palace." She grinned as she looked around the lobby as they moved towards the elevator. The multiple chandeliers shown brightly, and the expensive artwork casually accommodated the areas where there were comfortable sitting areas that looked rarely used.

They paused at the reception desk, and Fred announced, "We have an appointment with Victor Bellinger in the fifth-floor conference room."

The receptionist glanced at her list and said, "You may go right up, sir. He is expecting you."

They entered the glass-enclosed elevator. Fran stepped forward. "Let me push the magic button. This is exciting."

Fran delighted in pointing out several parks, buildings, and other objects of interest as they rose.

The door opened, and they were facing the entrance to the conference room. Fran sniffed the air. "They even have a pleasant air freshener here." Then she glanced inside the conference room window and saw Victor rise from his seat and indicate they should enter.

"Ms. Smith, I'm delighted you could come. I hope Fred told you that it was okay to bring a friend."

"Maybe if we have another meeting, but I'll let Pastor Fred be my bodyguard for this time," she said with a grin.

Victor grinned and said, "Well, I wasn't so confident, so I'd like to introduce you to my 'bodyguard.' This is David Johnson, an elder from our church."

After they had all greeted each other, Victor continued. "This is my humble abode. Please feel free to gaze out the window, and then let's sit around this smaller table over in the corner so we can have a good conversation. I've also set up an easel if we need it."

When they had seated, Victor continued, "Ms. Smith, I'd..."

Fran interrupted, "Mr. Bellinger, I'm comfortable calling adults by their last name as my mama taught me, but I'd be pleased if you would call me Fran."

"Fran it will be. Would you tell David a little about yourself?"

Fran shared a little about herself, ending with, "I've come from a family with a strong history of civil rights activity and generally fighting for justice and equality for all. I've just begun coming to Fourth Presbyterian because the youth group invited me, and I've heard that it is a caring church. I don't pretend to be perfect, and I need a church that, although imperfect, wants to offer a better life, even for imperfect people."

Victor and David stared at her for a moment, and then David said, "Welcome, Fran. I hope we can live up to your expectations. We are a good church and proud of our ministry on behalf of the poor, but we also want to avoid any actions that would sow division among our family."

Fran glanced at Fred, inviting him to continue. "Well, at least we didn't waste any time getting to our primary subject for this afternoon. We are here because we all have an investment in Fourth Presbyterian, and my personal interest is how we might hold on to different opinions but be united as a family of faith as we take our spiritual journey together."

"Look, Fred, I appreciate that we are all entitled to our differing opinions, and I don't object to your having brought Ms. Smith along to advance your cause..."

Victor held up his hand. "David, I think I explained to you that I was the one who invited Fran to participate. She brings some perspective that I think we need to hear. This wasn't Fred's idea; it was mine."

David grimaced and nodded his head. "I stand corrected, but I still don't understand why Fred has to bring politics into the church. It's just divisive and not part of what a church should be about."

Fred held out a hand towards Victor. "As you will recall, this all came about because of my recent sermon and Victor's strong response to it." Turning his head back to David, "In many ways, his thoughts are parallel to some of your thoughts, David."

Fred turned and continued, "To get this moving forward, let me ask you a question, Victor. You have a reputation for bringing disparate groups with contrasting perspectives together and forging a new direction. In outline form, what is your method for doing that?"

"Okay, I see where you are going with this, but I'll participate. In business, not necessarily the church, I think bringing differing opinions into the same room and forcing them to listen to each other is a little like mixing the proper chemicals together. You risk an explosion, but if you do it carefully, you can create something new that is very valuable."

"But not the church," David said. "We don't come to church to create something new. We come to be comforted and to grow closer to God and each other."

"Pardon me," Fran spoke up," but isn't the church supposed to help us with our sins and failures and to help us to get fresh starts?"

They all looked at her for a moment. Then Victor smiled, "Have you been coaching this young lady, Fred? She comes out with some pretty challenging ideas."

"My papa and mama don't go to church as often as they should," Fran continued, "but they have always been strong about the church being a home for sinners who are loved into wholeness. They told me lots of stories about the Pharisees being righteous and proud of their goodness and Jesus reaching beyond them to those who were left out. Isn't that what the church is about?"

Inside Fred was cheering, but outwardly he tried to keep a calm and attentive demeanor. He turned and winked at Victor. "I'm not the one who is bashing you over the head with the Bible, Victor."

"OK, OK, let's assume for a moment that we aren't playing win/lose but win/win. Let's also assume that plenty of people in the congregation agree with you and plenty share some of our opinions. How do we explore these issues without tearing the church apart?"

David clenched his hands as he spoke, "Keep politics out of it, I'd say. I understand that we are all sinners," he nodded at Fran, "but all this Black Power stuff is just stirring up division among us in society, and we don't need to bring it into the church."

"What if," Fred began, "we could figure out a way, just for Fourth Church, that we could admit that none of us were perfect? What if, by listening to each other, God might stretch us? What if by listening to different ideas, we might demonstrate to our society that there is a better way of living than always splitting up into opposing sides?"

"We might be able to pull that off in a small group like this, but how would you do that with 800 people, many of whom don't even know each other, let alone talk to each other?" Victor asked.

David shook his head. "That would be a miracle. All we do in this society is see who can dominate the other. It's a dog-eat-dog society. Do you really think a church can be any different?"

"I've got a couple of ideas, but they are rough and need to be shaped by a small group like this and then introduced to the congregation in a way that shows that all of us support the process and not just one side or the other."

"Fran, what do you think about this?" Victor asked.

"I think it's exciting. If we did something like this, I think I could even get my papa and mama to start coming back to church. My papa is a little bit of a firebrand, but I think his big problem is he thinks no one is listening. Imagine what could happen if 800 people learned to listen to each other and respect our differences. Wow, what a gift to offer the world!"

"Speaking of being beat over the head with a Bible, "said Victor, "I think there is something in there about the church spreading Good News. If you have an idea about how to do that, Pastor, I'm willing to listen."

"The people in our church are good people," said David. "But no one likes to be accused of being a racist. I even resent the implication. How are you going to get good decent people to listen to that sort of bullshit?"

Victor raised his hand to pause what was happening. "David,

there is a lady present."

"No, Mr. Victor, let him speak. I'm almost twenty-one years old, and I've heard plenty..." she nodded towards David, "of bullshit. One of the problems with what Pastor Fred is proposing is that from my experience, many White people are frozen in a bubble of," she raised two fingers of both hands and bent the fingers, "'niceness.' The real challenge is how to get NICE people to hear some uncomfortable truths that might even shake them up."

Victor nodded at Fran. "You are one tough cookie. If we were always hamstrung with being nice in my business, we'd never get off the dime. A truth that challenges is often uncomfortable. But I don't know how to get a whole church of diverse people to have that conversation."

"Look, Victor," David slapped the table with one of his hands, "It's all well and good for you to run one of your company meetings that way. Everyone knows you're the boss, and you hold the power. If you want rough and tumble, they'll go along. But that won't work in a church where there are eight hundred voices, and no one is the boss."

"He does have a point, Victor," Fred said with a smile. "If you said anything that offended them, I doubt if the first move of members of your group would be to gather in the parking lot and decide how they were going to get you fired."

"And who gets to define what is truth, anyway?" David paused, waiting for an answer from either man.

"At least he has the guts to try." Fran leaned forward and looked at Victor and David with an intense stare. "Do the two of you have the courage to hear him out and see if he can devise a way to get people both talking and listening to each other? Where's all this love of neighbor stuff?"

"I don't need a lecture on courage, young lady. I've fought more battles than you have had years to live," David glared at Fran.

Fred decided it was time to check in. "Okay, this is an example of what we need to try. David, I know you are a tough person, and I don't question your courage, but I wonder if you can tell Fran what you heard her say?"

David hesitated, sat up straighter. "I think she..."

"Tell her, not me."

"Oh, all right, I think you," David stared directly at Fran, "are saying that this racism crap you people are always whining about is some magical truth and that White people are a bunch of fragile idiots that would fall apart if they listened to what you are saying. We built this country, young lady, and we have a right to protect what's rightfully ours. I'm not saying there isn't some injustice in our society, but that doesn't mean that all of us are monsters. This racist bullshit goes both ways, and I'm sick of hearing about it. It's certainly not what I go to church to hear." David was almost shouting when he finished. He looked down at the table, took a deep breath, and said, "I'm sorry, Miss, I got a little carried away. I guess I'm just frustrated with all of this messing up my church."

Everyone, including David, looked a little shocked at his explosion. Fred cleared his throat. "Now, Fran, did David capture what you were trying to say to him and us?"

Fran, who was still staring wide-eyed, blinked a couple of times and then said, "I think he added a little more than what I was trying to say. But one thing he got right is that it is an issue of power. When people feel threatened, White or Black, they tend to fight back. The difference is that most White people either have more power or have access to power to shut Black people down.

"And just to be clear," Fran continued, "I'm a person, Mr. Johnson, not a whole race. I don't speak for all my people. And I strongly doubt that you speak for all White people, even all the White people at Fourth."

Victor spread his hands in a gesture of calming the atmosphere. He reached over to push a button on the table before them. "Dylis, would you be so kind as to bring in some water, coffee, and some sodas plus some ice and glasses, please?"

He turned to his guests, "First, Fran, I don't know where you are in school, but if you ever need a job, I want you to come and talk to me."

Fran blushed and stuttered a little. "Tha..., thank you, Mr. Victor, I'll do that."

"Second, Fred, I think we all need a little breathing room to think about this, but I'm interested in hearing about any plan you might come up with. I confess that I've become somewhat settled in my religion, but you've just given me a glimpse of another possibility. I want to hear more. And I hope, David, you will also stick with us through this process.

As he gazed at David, Victor continued, "You may have let your temper get away from you, but you are a smart man, and your perspective can keep us focused on what a lot of people are thinking in this church."

As they were all mumbling their assent, the door opened, and Dylis came in with the refreshments. As Dylis prepared the drinks, each person moved around the room, checking in with each other and assuring one another that their relationships were still intact.

Later, as Fred and Fran were driving toward her home, Fred took a deep breath and released it, "Actually, I think that went better than I expected. I sure am glad that your boyfriend, or maybe ex-boyfriend, brought you to our youth group. You were great in there."

Fran gave Fred a shy glance. "Do you think Mr. Victor was serious about a job possibility? I could use some extra money to pay for my school."

"Victor is a powerful man, and though we often disagree on some things, I've never seen him break his word. I think you can count on that as money in the bank. It's definitely worth following through on the offer."

 **FOR CHAPTER RESOURCES AND ADDITIONAL CONTENT, SCAN THIS QR CODE:**
SMcCutchan.Kartra.com/page/CHAPTER12

# CHAPTER 13

# IMPERFECT CHURCH

Charles, the stated clerk of the session, called Fred on Wednesday evening. "Fred, as I'm sure you are aware, there has been a pretty strong reaction to your sermon this past Sunday. Several of the elders have been virtually accosted with demands that they do something. I've received more than a dozen calls myself, and many of the other elders have received calls as well. I'd suggest we have an emergency meeting of the session to decide what we will do."

"Given the emails and even anonymous letters I've received, I'm very aware that people are stirred up. I agree that we need to discuss this as a session, Charles. What about Saturday morning at about 10 a.m. at the church?"

"I'm glad you agree, Fred. I'll issue the call for the meeting. I don't know what the hell you were thinking when you preached that sermon, but we need to deal with this post-haste."

Fred had expected, even wanted, people to be challenged by his sermon. Still, as he disconnected the phone, he wondered whether this was his Garden of Gethsemane moment and, more importantly, whether he had the courage to face it. He issued a brief prayer for that courage and then turned to find Lilly and tell her of the meeting.

In calling the elders, Charles made clear the purpose of the meeting was to discuss people's responses to the sermon and the general upset in the church.

"What do you think they are going to do, Fred?" Lilly asked. "Why don't you just hang a sign on the door reminding them that Jesus said that if the same person offended you four hundred and ninety times, you were supposed to forgive them. So, when a pastor reaches four hundred and fifty times, it'd be time to call a meeting."

Fred gave her a brief hug and a kiss on the cheek. Your slightly cynical humor has helped me keep perspective more than once, Lil. How was I so lucky to meet you?"

"You mean, after all these years, you still don't know how I manipulated that first meeting? You don't think it was hospital policy to slip your phone number into the pockets of handsome patients, do you?"

Early Saturday morning, as he prepared to leave for the church, he turned to Lilly. "Wish me luck; I'm going to try to practice what I preach. ¡Escúcheme! I'm going to try to listen to the pain and fear behind their words and see what effect it has."

"Just remember, you are worth being listened to as well. Don't go putting yourself down. It isn't wrong to stand up for the gospel. I think I've even heard my pastor say that once or twice."

Fred's shoulders relaxed, and he grinned. Not only did he think that was true, but he also knew that he would have to explain himself to Lilly when he got home, so he had better be on his good behavior.

Fred could appear strong for his wife, but as he began to drive towards the church, his thoughts were all over the place. The sermon was preached from his heart, but he knew every member of his congregation listened from their hearts as well. Each of them was filled with their own hopes and fears. He must prepare himself to listen both to the logic of what a person says and to the feelings underneath the words. He hoped he would be able to listen very deeply to each person who spoke.

As he parked his car and made his way to the church office, he was planning how to set up the seating arrangements so that people could see everyone. No one would hide in a back row. Each would be in front of all of the others. Each person who smiled in agreement or winced and disapproved would be broadcasting their message to all the rest. Nine elders, Karen, and the Stated Clerk, plus himself--that shouldn't be too hard to set up. He also wanted all of them to have a water bottle, a pen, and some paper.

About an hour later, he heard the cars begin to arrive. While the nine elders had other plans that they would have preferred to pursue on a Saturday morning, they had agreed to the meeting. As they entered the church, they had various responses to seeing Fred greeting them at the door. Some shook his hand formally and patted him on the shoulder as a sign of support. Some grimaced and shoved past him. Still, others looked at him and shook their heads as if to say, "What have you gotten us into?"

Fred opened with prayer and voiced his thanks for each of them interrupting their Saturday to attend. "While Charles will keep a running account of what takes place, our purpose is to allow each of you to share what you are feeling and to listen to each other. I'm going to try to practice what I call Active Listening. After each of you has spoken, I will try to summarize what I've heard to make sure I understand you. Certainly, if I've misunderstood or left something out that you feel important, please correct me.

"There is a bottle of water, a pen, and some paper at the base of your chair. While this is not a legislative meeting where we take votes, it is vital that we both hear and remember what was said among us."

There was a little shifting around in their seats. Several reached for their bottle of water and took a first swig.

"Okay, I'm not here to debate with any of you. I'm here to listen, not only to your words but also to your hearts. I'd suggest that we begin with Betty on my left and work our way around the circle until everyone has had a chance to express themselves."

Betty cleared her throat. "I've been a member for over thirty years and have been on the Session a couple of times. I've never seen such a mess. I'm just sick at heart that you have done this to my church."

"So, Betty," Fred began, "I hear you feeling upset, maybe even angry, that I preached a sermon that has caused such a negative response. And that you hold me responsible for possible damage to the church that you dearly love. Is that right?"

Betty nodded and added, "I love you, Fred, but what you did is just not right."

"I understand, Betty." He looked at Jerry, sitting next to Betty, and indicated that it was his turn.

"I'm fairly new to the church, Fred. I'm not even sure why the church elected me to the Session. I came from a church in the

Carolinas, and when we moved here, I heard that this was an active church and didn't just hide from society." He smiled and shook his head. "I guess I heard right, but I never expected this. But I'm here for you and will support you in any way I can."

"Jerry, your new, but you were attracted to this church because we had a reputation for active ministry in the community."

Jerry nodded and added, "And, while I don't understand all that is going on, you are my pastor, and I support you."

Fred nodded and turned to Wilford, who was sitting next to Jerry.

"I'm a banker, a successful one, and one of our prime mottoes is that you never upset the customer if it is at all possible to avoid it. I think you violated that motto, Pastor. You could have emphasized the importance of loving our neighbor or even forgiving our enemies without making your audience feel personally accused. In my business, you would have been called on the carpet and possibly fired."

"Wilford, you are saying that my sermon violated a commonsense rule of good business and may need to pay the consequence."

Wilford nodded, and Fred indicated that it was Martha's turn. "I was raised in a church where the pastor was always afraid he would offend someone. His motto," she nodded at Wilford, "was peace at any price. That took priority over Jesus, the Gospel, or integrity. I don't always agree with what Fred says, but he never fails to make me think. I think I've grown spiritually by being here. Thank you, Fred."

"Martha, you are saying that you value being challenged, and even when you disagree, you have grown spiritually from those encounters." He smiled his thanks.

David was next. "Most of you know that Fred and Victor Bellinger have already spoken about this. Both Victor and I came to that meeting full of steam, and then we were called up short by a young woman who has just begun attending this church. She made me climb out of my shell and start thinking about how what we decide to do here will have an impact beyond the walls of this church. I'm not very familiar with church language, but I think that is what is called making a witness. I'm not sure what we should do, but I think it's important that we accept responsibility for how our actions will reveal to others just what this faith is about.

After a pause, David continued, "And that's said after I learned from my several exchanges on this that I have some unconscious racial attitudes that I hadn't realized."

Before Fred had a chance to summarize David's comments, Curtis spoke up. "OK, OK, I get it. We all have a little prejudice here and there, but I don't think the church is the place to get into a political debate. All that Black Lives Matter crap and 'Whites get all the breaks' and 'protests in the street often result in violence' just doesn't belong in our worship services. If I want to know about that stuff, I can listen to the talk shows on the radio or read the Wall Street Journal. I come to church to ease my stress, not exacerbate it. If I keep hearing this type of stuff, I'll go back to the golf course for relief."

"Curtis, what I hear you saying is that you believe the role of the church is to help people feel comforted and reassured. And you feel so strongly about it that you would consider leaving the church and looking for your wellbeing on the golf course instead. Is that right?"

"Well, you could probably argue me out of that last part. I never could avoid hooking my drive, which probably caused me more stress than relieved it. But I think people should feel like a church is a safe place to come where they won't get into a bunch of political arguments and be shamed for having different opinions."

Luther spoke up next. "I guess I'm next. Hearing all of you is leaving me a little confused. I don't mind making good business decisions and approving different programs or outreach ministries. Plus, I confess I hadn't thought about this for a long time, but sometimes when I hear Fred or Karen read from the Bible, the same thought pops into my head: 'Wow, do you think people heard what was said?' All that stuff Jesus said about loving your enemy, not casting the other stone, and maybe the hardest one, 'Give to everyone who begs from you and do not refuse anyone who would borrow from you.' How would you like to hear that every Sunday, Wilford? I think we belong to a more radical group than we realize."

Fred stared at Luther for a moment and then said, "I'm not sure what we do with that, Luther, but I think you are suggesting that the Scriptures call us to a more radical obedience than we realize."

Dianna playfully punched Luther on the arm. "So how am I to follow that, big boy? It sounds like we have not even begun to probe what the church is supposed to be about. Maybe before we make any big decisions, we need to discuss what the church is really about. I can just see Jesus standing here, listening to us and shaking his head in frustration."

"So, Dianna, if I hear you correctly, you think we should make use of this moment to help guide the congregation in a church-wide reflection on what it means to be part of Christ's church."

Luther interrupted. "Ha! Fat chance you would ever get eight hundred people to even participate in such a discussion, let alone agree with each other."

Eugene, the youngest elder on the board, raised his hand. "I think I'm the last one to speak on this first round."

Luther waved his hand. "Sorry about that, Eugene. I yield the floor."

"Being one of the newer members and," he looked around the circle, "I guess one of the younger elders here." He paused again and then continued, "It always feels strange being referred to as an elder. Anyway, because of my work with technology, I think there are some ways that we might create a communication chain that engages the whole church. I could work with Karen on that."

"That would be great," Karen spoke up. "I already have some ideas that I would like to discuss with you."

Eugene continued, "But what I wanted to say is I think the younger generations, younger than me, are always both irritated and confused by all the divisions in the world and the church. We divide by race, sexual orientation, wealth, citizenship, and even Christian and non-Christian. I think half the world's conflicts could be eliminated if we got rid of the lines we are always drawing."

Several people nodded their heads as Fred began to feedback what he'd heard. "First, your willingness to share your tech gifts is greatly appreciated. Your main contribution is that lots of conflict in this world is caused by our penchant to divide people into artificial groups."

Martha pumped her fist in the air. "I'm with you there, Eugene. Maybe then we could all live up to our potential."

David lifted his head. "That's what frustrates me, Martha. Black Lives Matter, street protests, marching on the courthouse. If you people would just stop emphasizing our differences, maybe we could live in peace."

Martha smiled. "Oh David, why didn't I think about that. The next time I'm at a meeting of the women of the world, I'll put that at the top of our agenda."

Some looked a little confused, but David spoke up, "I wasn't talking about you being a woman. I was talking about you being..." David paused, lowered his head and said softly, "I'm sorry, Martha. I know you don't speak for all Black people, or," he grinned, "for all women for that matter. Maybe if we keep having these conversations, I'll cleanse my vocabulary of all my latent racist assumptions."

"It's OK, David," Martha reached over and patted his arm. "I know you are a good person at heart. The problem that we African Americans can never forget is that the majority of White people are good people but unconscious of how they participate in and support racist assumptions in our society."

"Can you expand on that?" Luther asked.

"Well, not to get into it too deeply, but almost all Blacks feel like we are living in this society as guests, not members. White citizens constructed the rules about what is proper or permitted, and we are mostly OK if we just go along to get along. But if we violate those expectations, then the power structure, even through unconscious powers, exacts its price."

"Explain that some more," urged Jerry.

"Well, for one example, I'll bet none of you who have children ever had to have THE TALK (she emphasized the words) where you had to explain to your children that they would likely be stopped by the police more than their White friends. When that happens, they must be incredibly careful -- always keep their hands in sight, never make sudden moves, and above all, don't make wisecracks. 'If you do, your very life could be in danger.'" She turned to look at them. "If you all moved to Russia, you might have to explain similar types of rules and advice. You might see all police as dangerous, but you don't have to do so in your own country."

Wilford spoke up. "My momma always said, 'do the crime, then you do the time.'"

"But I bet your mother never said, whether you do the crime or not, if you smart off to a cop, you might get yourself shot." Martha's voice took on a harder edge than before. "Just like now, I'm beginning to get upset, and I know that not being friendly and polite in these conversations can get you in trouble when you are far from being in charge. Fred, could we get back to the original discussion?"

"Of course, Martha, but you have offered us a valuable gift by being so honest with us."

Most all the elders nodded, smiled, and reached out and touched her if near her.

"Actually," continued Fred, "all of you have given a gift of spiritual leadership to the church this morning by having the discipline and care to listen to each other and try to build some understanding. Thank you very much."

"To address one elephant in the room, if it comes to that, we can have a discussion later about my future employment at the church. There were three parties to our agreement when I came here. The church, our presbytery, and I -- all three needed to approve my becoming your pastor. I hope we don't get there but, if we do, we would need to get the agreement of all three parties for a dissolution of that agreement. If necessary, I'll help us through that process.

"For now, however," Fred continued, "I'd like us to experiment with something that has rarely happened in recent times. You've just witnessed a group of twelve people politely listen and try to understand each other even though we have contrasting opinions and feelings about what is happening here. Imagine the impact on our society if we could demonstrate how 800 independent thinkers could do that in a way that strengthened rather than weakened the bonds that connect us."

"If you can pull that off," Betty smiled, "I'll bow at your feet and praise you to the highest heavens."

There was a wave of chuckles and a few "here, here's" around the circle.

"Thank you, Betty, but the truth is, I can't alone. I'm trusting that with God's help, we can."

"I wish you the best of luck, Fred, but I fear few of us are that holy," said Jerry. "If churches took that seriously, even here in in our city, we wouldn't have so much rioting in the streets."

"I agree that churches don't have a great history of demonstrating the love of Christ for each other, let alone society. If we did, we wouldn't be split into so many denominations and have so much division even in individual churches." Fred paused. "OK, here is a Bible quiz. Who can think of an example of an imperfect person or community being used by God for a greater good? You don't have to remember where it is in the Bible. Just reference the basic story."

There was an uncomfortable silence. Several people reached for their water bottles. Karen rose and left the room and returned with a box of donuts.

"An angel has visited us," said one.

"Just think, if my call committee hadn't had the wisdom to call Karen, we might be starving at this moment," said another.

Karen laughed and beamed as she distributed the donuts and napkins around the circle.

Then as they munched and thought, one finally spoke up. "I don't know the details, but I recall Fred telling us that Paul, once called Saul, was an enemy of the church?"

Another said, "And what about David? He was a real rascal. If you think about it, he broke almost all the ten commandments."

"Thomas doubted, Judas betrayed, James and John were power-hungry," Dianna chimed in. "Of course, if you notice, those were all men, but we'll save that conversation for another day."

"Uh, oh, now we really are getting into the political thicket," someone grumbled.

Fred held up both hands. "Peace, peace. Before we get into the battle of the sexes, I just want to point out that God is inclined to work through imperfect people and imperfect communities to accomplish great things. We won't do it perfectly, but the question is, do we trust God enough to give it a try?"

The conversation continued for another half hour, but what had begun in tension now became a community challenged by a vision of hope and promise.

**FOR CHAPTER RESOURCES
AND ADDITIONAL CONTENT,
SCAN THIS QR CODE:**
SMcCutchan.Kartra.com/page/CHAPTER13

# CHAPTER 14

# THE SERMON PROPOSAL

As Fred and Karen entered the sanctuary, they were aware that there was a heightened sound of people talking. As he looked around the room, he also recognized that he would be preaching to a packed sanctuary. He knew that there was no guarantee as to the results, but at least, whether they agreed or disagreed with him, they were going to give him a chance to explain what lay ahead.

His sermon was going to be part proclamation and part explanation of the proposal. They were also going to celebrate communion at the end. He hoped that would help remind all of them of their commitment to Christ and to each other.

As he and Karen took their seats, the choir continued their processional. They had chosen an arrangement from a familiar tune, "Where Cross the Crowded Ways of Life." He always liked that brief moment before he rose to guide the people. Few could ever understand that those fleeting moments before the service began were filled with a mixture of joy and sadness for almost any pastor. While you saw many solid, faithful members, you also saw people's wounds silently locked in pain —- a broken marriage here, a business deal or professional decision that would wound others there. Through counseling, Fred was aware of children locked in rebellion, a yet-to-be-revealed affair, court negotiations that would likely mean jail time and a shattered reputation. Some were angry at the church, at the pastor, at the session, and more than people knew, some were furious with God. Yet here they were. Often, just below their own awareness, there was a yearning for a word, a song, a prayer that could lift them out of their self-centered prisons and connect them with the Divine.

As his eyes swept the sanctuary, he suddenly saw Fran sitting with a group of college friends, White and Black, male and female. From their postures, he could tell that not all of them were familiar with this style of worship. As his eyes connected with Fran, he saw a brief smile touch her lips and an almost invisible lifting of her hand with a thumbs-up gesture. He uttered a silent prayer of gratitude for her support. His wife, his secretary, his Associate Karen, and now Fran were four women whom he could count on.

As the choir grew silent in their seats, Fred rose and entered the pulpit where he would lead them in a call to worship. Whatever each one had brought to this sanctuary from his or her daily life, and even their reactions to what had been happening this past week in the church, now, for a few moments, they would all be invited to redirect their thoughts and feelings towards a larger truth made available to them through Christ.

Call to Worship: 2 Corinthians 5:19-20a

Leader: God was in Christ, reconciling the world to God's self

People: God doesn't count our sins and imperfections against us

Leader: God entrusts the message of reconciliation to us.

People: So we are ambassadors for Christ

They continued with singing "All People that on Earth Do Dwell." Then Karen offered a beautiful prayer, slightly adapting verses of Psalm 51:

"Create in (us) a clean heart, O God,

And put a new and right spirit with (us)

Do NOT CAST (US) AWAY from your presence,

And do not take our holy spirit from (us)

Fred could not help but glance at different faces, particularly those who had been in such opposition to him. He wondered whether any of this was getting through to them. Or, as Victor had said earlier, did they just feel like they were being beaten over the head with the Bible?

Regardless, they confessed their sins and were assured of their forgiveness.

As they approached the sermon, Fred could feel the tension rising. He first opened the Bible to Luke 10:27 and read Jesus' declaration of the Great Commandment. Then he read 1 Corinthians 13 about the nature of love.

Then he looked out at the congregation for almost a minute without saying anything. Then he slowly said, "Escúcheme," and then he repeated it a couple more times. Then he smiled and asked if they would try to say it back to him. When they got it down, he said, "I know this is a little strange, but would you turn to a couple of neighbors and say to them 'escúcheme'?

"As you know, I preached a sermon from this pulpit last week that got a fair amount of response..." He paused about ten seconds and then added, "both positive and negative."

There were several chuckles and nods, some with smiles and some with frowns. "Some people expressed support for what I said, and some were sharply negative, suggesting that the best thing I could do was promptly resign and leave town."

From several spots in the sanctuary, people voiced their opinions. Some people booed, while others shouted several phrases such as, "We have your back, Rev," or "Let them leave; You stay."

Fred had never done this before, but he stepped out of the pulpit and stood in the center of the chancel facing the congregation. As he moved towards that position, he raised his hand in a calming gesture and said, "I appreciate your support, but this is not a political convention where we choose up sides. We are a church family. Though that sermon came from a place deep in my soul, it is vital to our soul as a church that we learn what you just said to your neighbor -- ESCÚCHEME."

He had their complete attention now. And they were very silent, waiting for his next words. "For those of you who know Spanish, you heard the word that roughly translated means 'Listen to me!' And it is in what linguists call the imperative or command form. In essence, you aren't asking your neighbor to listen to you, you are strongly telling them to listen to you; they are saying the same to you. Can you imagine the impact on this world if everyone listened to their neighbors, not just to their words but to their souls?"

Again, he paused for a few seconds and gazed around at those who sat before him. "When you take seriously what Christ commanded his disciples, including us, and reflect on how Paul described what love is all about, don't you hear with an even deeper understanding that it begins here in the church? We have a witness to make in this community. And we must pay particular attention to what our neighbors hear as they see and experience our behavior as a church. That, I believe, is where in our current society the pain of racism confronts us.

"And it doesn't mean that our neighbor or we are always right. What I said last Sunday came from the depth of my soul, out of the pain I felt in watching what I describe as racism. It became very personal as I stood by my friend's side as he waited to see whether his son would live or not. That doesn't mean that those who were upset or objected to what I said don't have souls and deep feelings that also need to be heard. If we believe, as the Scriptures say, that what God was doing in Christ was reconciling the world to God's self and not counting their sins against them, then we, too, need to lead with forgiveness and not judgment. Our souls -- each of us -- belong to God. What God values, we dare not dismiss lightly."

In some corner of his mind, he became aware that both the frowns and the smiles had left people's faces, and they were all leaning forward and listening with a deep intensity. Some were weeping, which included some he assumed had been among those who deeply objected to what he had said before.

"There are several profound truths that I think the Church, beginning with this church, needs to focus on in this chaotic world in which we live.

"First, in the entire biblical story, God doesn't seek to speak the Divine truth only through perfect people. In fact, God seems to prefer to funnel God's truth through ordinary, often imperfect people and everyday events. At the end of this service, we are going to participate in the celebration of communion. That event makes use of two very common elements, bread and juice, to convey Divine truth. And if you recall the description of Jesus breaking the bread and sharing the wine on that fateful night, the disciples were far from perfect people, but they were together in community.

"Secondly, God doesn't seem to always want to shy away from conflict. I confess that I don't like conflict, particularly in the church. Throughout all my ministry, I've struggled with the tension between saying and doing what I believe in my heart of hearts is true and doing or saying what will please people." He paused a couple of seconds. "Although you may not think that's true at this moment." Several people chuckled or shook their heads, but they were still listening intensely.

"What I've come to believe is this. You shouldn't seek conflict because that is hardly practicing the art of listening to others; still, God often can use conflict as a space for a blessing. Often conflict shakes us out of our comfort zone, and sometimes it allows some room for God to get a word in edgewise. That doesn't mean that those who oppose us are right. It means that God is not defeated by either of our opinions; further, if we will listen intensely to each other, God can give birth to a whole new understanding using imperfect people as a channel to new insight.

"Jesus didn't shy away from conflict and often used it to help people to come to a new understanding. For example, Jesus was challenged because he interacted with sinners and not the 'GOOD PEOPLE.' His response was, 'Those who are well have no need of a physician, but those who are sick; I have come to call not the righteous but sinners.' That does suggest that if Christ calls us to be a part of this church, that might indicate that we are all sinners." He again paused briefly, scanned the congregation, and smiled.

Again, there were some chuckles from different sections of the sanctuary and some brief smiles of agreement.

"The Good News is that we don't need to have all the right answers and perfect behaviors to be close to Christ. Christ accompanies imperfect people as we strive to be present to others who also struggle with difficult faith questions. We are in this together, and Christ is present in our less-than-perfect answers as long as we are also willing to be present to other less-than-perfect people. What we are trying to do in this conversation is to be humble enough as a community that we can grow to love each other as a community. We are neighbors, and even when it's difficult, we need to be loving towards each other.

"I certainly invite you to share your personal thoughts and feelings with me, Karen, and the session, but I want to see if we cannot listen to the whole congregation as well. Through our diverse and far-from-perfect thoughts and feelings, actions, and behaviors, what is God seeking to express through this part of the Body of Christ? I don't have all the details worked out, and it certainly will need to be modified as we go along. Still, I'm asking you as a congregation to cooperate with us by using technology to facilitate a congregation-wide conversation.

"As a framework, or to use computer language, as a template for our conversation, I want to suggest that we consider that what we are experiencing has its parallels in the wilderness experience in the Bible. Like them, we have had our familiar society shaken, and we are living in uncharted territory -- not only in the church but also in our community. To be realistic about it, there are very few clear signposts telling us where to go in the wilderness, and it is full of dangers and threats. The Israelites faced the dangers of hunger, thirst, and poisonous snakes, along with many other challenges. Real progress in their journey often required courage, sacrifice, and frequent conflicts among them and with their leadership. But what sustained them was a vision of what lay ahead and learning to trust God who was leading them.

"I don't think any of you would disagree with our shared hope that humanity could move past our often petty and sometimes major divisions; that we could live in a society that brought out the best in every individual as a valued child of God. We want to live in communion with the rich diversity God has created and rejoice in the beauty of creation that lifts our spirits. The question for all humanity is how we face adversity and how we learn to trust, even in moments of tragedy, in the God who leads us.

"We will be communicating with you about further details about how to accomplish this, but in the meantime, I invite you to escúcheme among yourselves and trust that God is faithful to us, imperfect as we are, and wants us to discover our portion of that Promised Land.

"As a sign of our communal love, I invite you to share the bread and wine that unites us in Christ. Let us pray together." Fred led them in the great prayer of thanksgiving, and the elders approached to receive the elements that were distributed among the people. He hoped he wasn't over-projecting his own feelings onto the congregation, but he sensed that there was an unusual depth to this celebration of communion.

He was just about to close with prayer when he looked towards the back of the sanctuary and saw a tall, thin Black man begin to come down the center of the aisle. At first, he couldn't believe his eyes. He wondered if he wasn't experiencing an illusion born out of his emotional exhaustion this past week. But he recognized the big smile and raised hands of his friend, Tony Southgate, limping down the aisle and climbing the chancel steps.

All he could do was open his arms, and both men embraced as tears came down Fred's cheek. Tony turned towards the congregation as he rose to his feet. "Ladies and gentlemen, or better yet, Brothers and Sisters in Christ, I am the Reverend Tony Southgate. While we still have a way to go, I think my son, Eric, will recover. I want you to know that if you will join Fred, my church and I would be honored to travel with you on this wilderness journey."

With a glance at Fred, who was still speechless, Tony asked "With your permission, pastor, I would like to pronounce the benediction?" When Fred nodded, Tony continued, "Go out into the world in peace; have courage; hold on to what is good; return no one evil for evil; support the weak; help the suffering; honor all people; love and serve the Lord, rejoicing in the power of the Holy Spirit. And let the people say..."

And the whole congregation shouted "AMEN," and then they rose and burst out in applause. The organist didn't even try to play a postlude.

**FOR CHAPTER RESOURCES AND ADDITIONAL CONTENT, SCAN THIS QR CODE:**

SMcCutchan.Kartra.com/page/CHAPTER14

# CHAPTER 15

# THIN MOMENTS

The receiving line was filled with a lot more joy this time. There would likely be lots of different reactions among the congregation as they proceeded, but right at the moment, they felt like they were moving in a positive direction. Quibbles could come later, but now was a time to celebrate and affirm each other as a church.

Fred had quickly asked Tony to stand with him and Karen to greet the people. People rapidly warmed to the idea to show hospitality to their neighbor. Like many thin moments in Fred's recent life, he recognized that Tony's presence at this time opened a new chapter in his growing commitment to invite the congregation to respond to racism creatively. It would be a while before they were ready; yet, when it was appropriate, they would have a built-in community to support their efforts in adapting a Truth and Reconciliation strategy as they reached out into the larger community.

As exhausted as he was, he also felt renewed energy and excitement about talking in depth with Tony. When the last hand was shaken, they both fell into each other's arms and slowly walked with Karen back to the church's office suite.

Lilly was waiting in the hallway. Karen paused and reached out a hand to Fred. "With Lilly watching so there is no misinterpretation, I would like to give you a big hug. While there have been moments when this wasn't true, at this moment, I am proud to be a pastor and to be your partner in ministry."

Fred beckoned Lilly to join them, and as she approached, he turned and enveloped Karen in his arms. "Never doubt that I am equally proud that you are my Associate. We have a ton of work to do in the coming days, but I hope you and your family will find some relaxing and fun things to do during the rest of the day."

Both Lilly and Tony joined in the group hug.

Fred invited Tony to join him and Lilly for lunch, but Tony demurred. "First, you and Lilly need to go home, have a bite to eat, and then do whatever you do to relax, including maybe even a brief nap. Second, I rushed out of our service with only a quick word to Ariel that I would see her at home before one. After two services this morning and the emotional scene in which I just participated, I need some rest as well. Call me in about an hour, when both Lilly and Ariel are there with calendars in hand, and we will plan to meet for dinner when we are better rested."

As Tony turned to leave, a car screeched to a halt in front of the church. Fred felt a tightening of his stomach, remembering what had happened after church last Sunday. He was about to push Lilly back inside the church and shout out a warning to Tony when Fran emerged from the car.

Fran noticed his body movements and laughingly called out, "No, Pastor Fred, this isn't a gang attack this time. Or if it is going to come, we got here first."

"It's not the first time that you have surprised me, Fran. It's good to see you. What's up?"

"First, Pastor Fred, that was an awesome service. I was chilled to the bone. I almost shouted 'Amen, Hallelujah,' but then I remembered I was in a honkie church -- Damn, I've got to stop saying that." And then she hesitated and smiled, "and I guess I shouldn't have said 'Damn' either. I think you've got a lot of work to do to shape me up. But that wasn't why I came back."

"We'll work on your reformation later. What brought you back so quickly?"

"You saw the several friends I was with during the service? When we left the church, we went out to Burger King to get a bite to eat. While we were eating, we came up with an idea that might help you."

Tony and Lilly had circled back and were listening as Fran spoke.

"My friends and I are all in a sociology class at the City Community College. We heard you say you wanted to engage the whole church in a conversation about racism. Our professor is all hyped about using technology to build community. Since racism destroys community and you said that church is supposed to be about learning to love each other, what if we used technology to help you build an anti-racist community in your church? It would make a great class project for us, and I'm sure you are going to need some extra workers to help you."

Lilly squealed in delight and clapped her hands. "That's fantastic, Fran. I've been stewing about how Fred and Karen were going to be able to pull this off, and you've just become my angel in distress."

She turned to Fred. "You keep having more of what you call your thin moments like this, and I might become a believer yet."

He turned to look at Tony, who was grinning back. "Do you ever wonder why God chooses women to announce God's good news in this world, Fred? First, there was Mary at the birth, and then there was Mary at the tomb. You wouldn't happen to have Mary as your middle name, young lady?"

"No, but my mother's mother is called Mary. Would that work?"

"Works for me," Fred said. "Fran, I need to do a little more planning, but it would be wonderful to draw upon your help as well as that of your friends and professor. I'll call you in a couple of days, and we'll set up a planning meeting."

"Cool, I'll tell my friends. Now go and have some downtime with Ms. Pastor, Fred." She waved and jumped in her car and sped off.

"Say hello to Ariel, Tony, and we'll call you and set up a date," said Lilly. "And now I've got to get Mr. Thin Moment home and get some food in him."

As Lilly drove Fred home, she could see the combination of excitement and complete exhaustion competing with each other. "When we arrive, there is a small sandwich and some fruit in the refrigerator. I expect that I will drop you off at the front door, and by the time I put the car in the garage and close everything up, you will have consumed that food and laid down on the bed. I'll check on you shortly after four. Oh, and turn off your phone."

"I don't even have the energy to make a smart aleck response. Thank you for everything."

She pulled up in front of the house, and he slowly got out of the car. "See you in a couple of hours."

As Lilly entered the house, she saw Fred about to close the bedroom door. He glanced up and saw her enter. "Nice sandwich. I almost tasted it as it chased after the blueberries down my throat."

She smiled as he gently closed the door. She went to the fridge and got her sandwich and a glass of milk. "Whew!" she said. "I may be a recovering racist, but I'm a grateful one. Now, if Ariel and I can keep our men in check, we might have an interesting journey." She turned on some soft music, sat on her couch, and between nods, took occasional bites of her sandwich.

At four, she gently opened the bedroom door. Fred was just beginning to stir. "I see your internal alarm clock is still working," she said as she moved in to hug him.

"I called Tony and Ariel, and we've agreed that tomorrow evening would be an excellent time to meet at the Silver Slipper about six-thirty for a good meal and conversation. I told them I was fairly sure that you were free, but I'd let them know if there was a conflict."

"That's great, Lil. I wanted to talk with them before we moved ahead. I'm going to call Victor, David, and Fran and see if they can meet with Karen and me Tuesday afternoon. It's beginning to come together slowly, and I don't want too much time to elapse before the next step."

"You certainly had them revved up this morning. I think they could feel both your sincerity and your willingness to listen. Where'd you get that wilderness image? I think that it has real possibilities."

"I've always liked that story. Early in my ministry, I was fascinated by how reluctant Moses was to take on the leadership role. He wasn't a good speaker; he was sure people wouldn't listen to him; he'd already messed up badly in his early life; and on and on. Each time, God reminded him that God would go with him. Finally, God got a little weary of all his excuses and essentially said, 'Just get on with it. I'll handle the problems.' Whenever I feel inadequate, which is more often than even you realize, I just recall that story.

"I don't know where this is going, Lil, and if it hadn't been for Eric getting shot, I'd probably still be worried about how to soften what I want to say so that I won't offend anyone.  Somehow it just feels like most of our churches are wandering in the wilderness right now, not knowing for sure where they should be going. The story just seems to fit, and every time I try to make excuses, I hear this whisper, 'Just get on with it.'"

"OK, big Mo, you've crossed your Red Sea, and we'll journey together. However, I'm not sure about my being able to imitate Miriam's dance. If I tried doing something like that in front of the congregation, I think they might really freak out."

"You might be surprised. I'll hold that image in my mind while I call Victor, David, and Fran to see what we can set up for Tuesday afternoon."

"Why don't you include Tony in the conversation?"

"We can talk about that when we get together Monday evening, but I think it might be best for the White church to get their act together first before they venture out. Our people are moderately progressive but rather trapped in what I'd call "niceness." Their image of racists are people dressed in white sheets, carrying torches, and chewing tobacco. They'd be careful about using overtly bigoted language in an interracial church meeting, but underneath the surface, there is a lot of latent prejudice that we need to face honestly."

"You're the Bible person but isn't there someplace where it talks about not being conformed to the world but focusing instead on renewing our minds or something like that?"

"OK, Lil, another text for a sermon. Soon I won't even have to look for texts. I'll just listen to my wife."

"Now, there is a novel idea!"

**FOR CHAPTER RESOURCES AND ADDITIONAL CONTENT, SCAN THIS QR CODE:**
SMcCutchan.Kartra.com/page/CHAPTER15

# CHAPTER 16

# A WILDERNESS JOURNEY

Karen and Fred had their meeting on Monday to talk about where they thought this might go and what type of questions might be useful to start with.

"I like using the image of the wilderness," said Karen. "First, the average member is less familiar with the Hebrew Scripture so that they may read it with fresh eyes. And, since it's not Gospel, they might feel more freedom to play with the images and possible ways to interpret them. One of the parallels I saw immediately is that we are all facing an uncertain future. Those people wondered where their next meal or drink was coming from, and didn't they also get attacked by a bunch of serpents?"

"I haven't seen any serpents around recently," suggested Fred.

"Oh, yeah? What about some of those emails and late calls in the night? I talked to Lilly the other night about some of her recent experiences. Sounds like we got our share of snakes in the grass."

"OK, OK, I get your point. And to continue your metaphor, maybe we could use some manna in our desert."

Karen went over to the candy and coke machine. "Don't see any manna in there, but they do have a Snickers and a Coke. Will that serve in the interim? You choose, and I'll buy."

"I get the larger salary. How about me buying?" Fred reached in his pocket for his wallet.

"Not this time, Reverend. This last Sunday's sermon deserves a reward. I'm not a quail delivering manna, but chocolate always feeds my soul. Make your choice."

Fred accepted the gift, and Karen brought the snack and soda to the table where they'd been sitting. She pulled out a chair facing Fred. "I do have a question, though."

"Lay it on me," Fred sat down and took a sip of the soda.

"I've only been ordained about five years, while you've been a pastor for what, about twenty years? I've had more than one time when I just wanted to throw it all up in the air and walk away. I'm not sure how people survive the ministry for a whole career. I read an article the other day that suggested that the rise among clergy in health problems, depression, and even suicide has risen dramatically in the last decade. My family deserves better than a depressed mother walking around. How do you keep it up, Fred?"

"The same way those former slaves kept walking across the wilderness. They had a compelling vision of a Promised Land ahead of them. As Viktor Frankl wrote, you give a person a 'why' and they can endure almost any 'how,' but you take away that hope or why then almost any challenge is too much."

"That's deep, Fred, but where do we find that vision that pulls our people forward?"

"I've been thinking about that. Think about that graffiti on our wall."

"You mean that Spanish phrase that meant something like 'listen to me'?"

"That's the one. I was talking about this last night with Lil, and she said something that sparked an idea. She heard me grumbling about it, and she said, 'You don't even get the majority of them to come to worship at the same time; how are you going to get them all to listen to you?'"

"I agree with Lilly, and even the ones who do come to worship, don't always listen to you."

"I'm reaching for even a bigger goal. What if we could get them to not only listen to us but to listen to each other?"

"They don't even listen to themselves when they are spouting all that garbage!"

"Well, that's where you come in, my esteemed Associate."

Karen was taking a drink when Fred was speaking and immediately snorted it up all over the table. Even as she began to mop up the mess, she turned and stared at him. "What in blazes are you talking about?"

"It's just an idea, but you have some technical skills that could help. What if we used the Internet to engage the whole congregation to join in a conversation about where God might be calling us as a church?"

"I'm not sure most members even think about God's call in their lives, let alone where God is calling them as part of a church." She hesitated. "Sorry to be so cynical."

Fred stood up and took another Coke out of the cooler. "This might require some more Coke while I explain it to you."

I'll try not to spit this one around the room," Karen said as she accepted the bottle.

While we did have a huge attendance this past Sunday, there is never a time when the whole congregation is present at the same time. But we could send a message to all of them."

"Because of the strong reaction to the last two sermons, I suspect that most people would read whatever message we sent," mused Karen.

"Let's take advantage of that. What if we acknowledged that we are aware that my previous sermons and the whole issue of racism have stirred up some concern about who we are as a church and where we are going on our spiritual journey together. We recognize that some disagree with my sermons, and some people don't even think our church should be involved with societal issues like this."

"At that point, no one would disagree, and they would be interested in reading the next paragraph," said Karen.

"Exactly, and that next paragraph would suggest that we would like to treat this as an opportunity rather than a problem. We will talk together about what it means for a diverse group of people to try to grow in our awareness of where God might be leading us."

Karen's forehead wrinkled as she considered what Fred was saying. "If we could get them to agree to participate, it would be a whole lot better than dividing up into groups and shouting at each other. But how do you get 800 people to come together to talk and listen to each other?"

"At least, to begin with, they don't have to come together; in fact, it might be better if they didn't. We have an email list of all the members. From time to time, we can use a program like Zoom and even Zoom groups to get them to meet in small groups."

Fred could begin to see Karen's eyes shine, and her body movements suggested she was becoming excited. "I can help with the tech questions, but how do we get them to talk to each other rather than at each other and at us."

"I began with yesterday's sermon. We can expand the idea in our newsletter and build on the wilderness journey's image and its association with our experience with the monsters of hurt, conflict, discomfort, and strong opinions. We can make it like a congregation-wide game.

"We tell them," Fred continued, "that we are going to begin with drawing on the memories of each of our experiences that drew us together as a church. We'll send them an email each Tuesday morning, requiring no more than a three-sentence response. We tell them that Fran Smith, who has been attending our youth group and worship services, has three other friends from her sociology class at the City Community College, who will help summarize what members have sent in. As part of her class project, she and her friends will create a composite image of our community that will be sent back out to the whole church."

"That's good. The summaries will seem more objective because outsiders make it part of an academic class."

Fred took a sip of his soda. "I haven't thought all this through, but I think we share the basic picture of where we are going from the beginning. We tell them that we will build a corporate image of our diverse church and assume that God is actively involved in our lives. We want to explore whether we can expand our awareness of what that might mean. We also tell them from the beginning that they can withdraw at any time they want to, but we trust that if we act in faith and with lots of prayer, we might grow in our faith and courage as a church. We also say that every month or so, we will have a Zoom Congregational meeting in which people can share their reaction to the process and how we might best proceed."

"If it gets going," Karen said with growing enthusiasm, "we can even use our litanies and prayers to recall various aspects of the wilderness experience and other relevant scriptural passages to reinforce our process. Wouldn't it be great to be a part of a church that faced issues realistically but with confidence that God was leading us to form an even more vital, lively, confident church that faced uncertain times unafraid?"

"Okay," Fred said, "You work on the technology, and I will work on better describing the process. Then maybe we can run it by Victor and David, our loyal opposition, to see if we can get their support."

"Since their explosions resulted in this process, they'd certainly be the place to start. The good news is that I think Saturday's meeting secured general support and maybe even some flexibility in how we proceed."

"I agree; however, I want to make one thing very clear. This all started because of something I did. I want you always to feel free to step aside at any point that you feel uncertain about what we are doing."

"I wonder if Moses made that speech to Arron," she chuckled. "Ezekiel and I talked about this, and we are in sync with the program. I'll tell you if that ever begins to change. Now I need to let you have some time to think about the next steps, and I will do a little research on possible computer programs that might help."

As she left the room, Fred heard her talking on her phone to her husband, "You were right, Zeke. I can't wait to tell you some of the next steps that Fred is suggesting."

Several hours later, Karen came bouncing into Fred's outer office. "Alice, is Fred available? I've got a fun way to begin our congregational conversation."

"You look like you've discovered your inner child and want to go out and play."

"Almost, it's a game we used in the youth group, and I think it would be a blast to play it as a whole church. If you have time, I'd love for you to hear about it."

Just then, Fred's door opened, and he stuck his head out. "What's going on out here? It sounds like the two of you are having far too much fun for me to be left out."

"Your profoundly serious Associate thinks she has discovered the key to happiness for the congregation. And she wants me to monitor the conversation to make sure you are listening very seriously. Escúcheme!"

"It will require a slight change in the framework that you had proposed. Have you ever heard of Survey Monkey?"

When Fred nodded, Karen continued. "A couple of years ago, we played a game in the youth group called <u>Majority Rules</u>. Since we want to both cause the congregation to relax and get into some serious thinking simultaneously, I think we should use Survey Monkey. It's not expensive for the numbers we will be addressing."

Karen began to hand out several sheets of paper. "We can tinker with the questions, but the idea is for the whole congregation to build up anticipation as to the results and, in their subconscious, begin to really think about what the church is.

"We can explain that we want to have some fun exploring how people think about certain issues," she continued. "We ask them to answer quickly and then return the questionnaire right away. Explain that there is not a right answer. We'll be curious both about the majority's answer and the variety in responses. This is not a legislative process but merely a recording of first impressions. The technology will allow each person to choose only one answer for each question. Once the surveys have been returned, we will tabulate the answers and report the results to the whole congregation."

"Sounds interesting," said Fred, "but of course, this all depends on the questions that we send out.".

"I adapted some old questions that we had used in the youth group to create a sample. Let me share them with you. We can always tinker with them as we go, but this will give us the idea. Take a moment to read over the entire set of questions and suggested answers.

## MAJORITY RULES QUESTIONS FOR BUILDING OUR COMMUNITY

1. To nurture a warm, welcoming church, all members should commit to:

>A. Speaking to at least seven people before they leave the sanctuary.

>B. Taking notice of and speaking to people they can't call by name.

>C. Always sitting in the same place, so people around them are familiar.

>D. Praying by name for members who seem lonely.

2. To lessen conflict and create harmony, pastors should:

>A. Avoid preaching on Scriptures that might be controversial.

>B. Only preach on subjects about which everyone agrees.

>C. Acknowledge potential disagreements about points made and encourage further conversation.

>D. Allow people to vote on which parts of the Gospel they like and preach accordingly.

3. To build transparency concerning church finances, the leadership should:

>A. Always report on and invite feedback on major expenditures.

>B. List by name and amount all pledges to the church.

C. Identify the faith principles we want to proclaim through our budget.

D. Encourage open conversation about expenditures as a faith issue.

4. The biggest contributor to distrust among church members is:

    A. Inadequate communication.

    B. Feeling that only a few people make all the decisions.

    C. Not understanding how decisions are made in the church.

    D. Not holding a shared vision about the nature and mission of the church.

5. Characteristics of a successful preacher are:

    A. Ability to preach sermons that inspire but don't offend.

    B. Preach sermons grounded in the Bible.

    C. Preach with integrity even when it offends but be open to feedback.

    D. Preach sermons that address personal issues but avoid commenting on social issues.

6. Cynicism and distrust are reduced in a congregation when:

    A. Diverse opinions are heard and respected.

    B. Controversial issues are not discussed.

    C. People accept that none of their opinions are perfect in God's eyes and continually seek to grow in understanding.

    D. People are committed to a shared vision of the

church's mission.

7. The primary reason churches split is:

A. Refusing to accept that we are all sinners and need to forgive each other continually.

B. Choosing to emphasize right beliefs over loving behavior.

C. Refusing to accept as priority Jesus' command that we be one.

D. Allowing personal beliefs to take precedence over being faithful to the church.

8. Loving your enemy is most difficult when:

A. Your enemy is from a different culture.

B. Your enemy belongs to your church but has different beliefs.

C. Your enemy treats you with contempt.

D. Your enemy affirms a different faith.

9. You know you can trust your pastor if:

A. The pastor totally agrees with your opinions.

B. The pastor is committed to interpreting Scripture and faith with integrity.

C. The pastor prays daily to be a faithful pastor and obedient to God.

D. The pastor is unafraid to preach with integrity but also listens sensitively to those who disagree.

10.The hardest part of the Lord's Prayer to accept is:

    A. That God's will will be done on earth.

    B. That God will provide our daily bread, and we need not succumb to greed.

    C. That God's forgiving us of our sins is affected by our willingness to forgive the sins of our neighbor.

    D. That asking God not to lead us into temptation will contribute to God's delivering us from evil.

Both Fred and Alice became so intrigued with the questions that aside from some intermittent laughter, there was little sound as Karen fidgeted, waiting to hear their reaction.

"That is absolutely brilliant!" exclaimed Fred. "The whole congregation, regardless of their feelings about our recent dialogues, will get caught up in the game and enjoy anticipating the final results."

Karen saw that Alice was nodding agreement enthusiastically, so she continued. "If Victor and David back us, then Fran and her friends could easily tabulate the results and report them with percentage points -- thirty percent believe this and sixty percent this, and so forth."

"I think you have a winner, Karen."

"That will be a great beginning, but then the question is how we proceed from there. Once we get directly into the racism issue, it will get a little dicier, said Fred."

"I'll let you work on that, Moses. This will get us to the Red Sea, but you will have to wave your staff to part the waters. I promised Zeke I'd meet him for a late lunch and bring him up to date."

 **FOR CHAPTER RESOURCES AND ADDITIONAL CONTENT, SCAN THIS QR CODE:**
SMcCutchan.Kartra.com/page/CHAPTER16

# CHAPTER 17

# A MEAL TO RELAX

Lilly Livinggood thought about the evening before them as she laid out her outfit and prepared to take a shower. She glanced at herself in the mirror. She was pleased that she had been able to maintain her weight over the years. "Being sexy is not your best feature," she said to the figure in the mirror, "but it's still fun to catch Fred watching as I get dressed or prepared for bed in the evening." As she had to focus more energy on rearing the kids, she had cut her hair shorter and reduced the amount of makeup she used. Now, though, as Lilly looked at herself, she fluffed her short hair and thought, maybe it's time to grow it out again while I still can.

She grinned. "You are really full of yourself this evening, aren't you? I guess that is how you react to stress." She thought about the evening ahead as she moved towards the shower. The last couple of weeks had been almost overwhelming, but one good blessing to come out of it was her new friendship with Ariel Southgate. She thought back on that painful night that seemed to be both a year ago and last night at the same time. It began with that late-night phone call from Ariel Southgate and Fred rushing to the hospital to support Tony as he waited to know his son's fate in surgery.

Since that night, their lives were challenged as they had never been before. Fred might still lose his position at Fourth, her life was threatened, her daughter had been accosted at school, the church was in turmoil with some possibilities of splits; yet through it all, she had seen strengths and support from members that both surprised and gave her courage, no matter what happened.

One of those surprises was meeting and becoming close friends with Ariel Southgate. She had known and been friendly with several Black women before, but she realized the vast difference between being friendly and being real friends. Real friends could share their hurts and fears, their joys, and dreams -- even occasionally their fantasies and weird thoughts without being afraid. They probably hadn't quite arrived at that last stage yet, but it seemed possible. In the process, she was beginning to realize that while they shared some similarities -- like being women, pastor's wives, and mothers of children -- there were some aspects shaped by their racial differences that she might never understand. Still, in just a couple of weeks, she realized that she could trust Ariel, and she was determined to offer her the same trustworthiness.

As she picked up her outfit from the bed, she chuckled. I'd bet a thousand dollars that no matter what I wear, Ariel will be both more stunning; at the same time, Ariel will somehow be relaxed in accepting me no matter what I wear. However, as she walked towards her closet, she thought, I might change this one in for something a little fancier. After all, when she and Ariel had talked about where to go for dinner, they had agreed that after what they had been through, they deserved a nice restaurant. When they informed their husbands, both men smiled, shook their heads, and mentioned tough women knowing how to get their reward.

As she was applying the last touches to her makeup, Fred came through the door. He glanced at her and said, "Wow, I was wondering what I should wear. Now I think I need to take a quick shower and choose my best suit."

She laughed lightly. "It is already laid out on the bed. While Ariel might outshine us, I suspect both of you preacher types will look respectable in your preacher suits."

Later, as they were driving to the restaurant, Lilly asked, "Are there any particular things I should be aware of, or subjects I should avoid?"

"You'll do fine, but I suspect that if we listen seriously, we may both learn a lot not only about Black thinking but also about what White people may be thinking."

"What do you mean?"

Tony once said that one effect of racism in our society is that Black people are never allowed to forget that they are the minority and must always be alert to the unexpected. That requirement to always be alert is one reason Black people have higher symptoms of blood pressure, heart problems, strokes, etc."

"Ironic, isn't it? People talk about seeing some Black teenagers on the street and getting nervous, but Black people face that tension almost everywhere they go. Ariel was telling me the other day that she walked into a department store wearing casual sweats, and almost every aisle she walked down, a security guard just happened to walk by. That's awful."

Fred nodded as he turned into the parking lot. "Lots of things are awful, but where possible, let's try to have some fun tonight. All of us need it."

As they approached the restaurant's hostess station, a spirited Black hostess greeted them with a large smile. "I'll bet you are the Livinggoods, and you are here to meet the Southgate couple?"

As they both smiled in assent, she took two menus and indicated that they should follow her. "They just arrived, and they described you perfectly -- she hesitated slightly and glanced at Lilly, "especially you, Mrs. Livinggood. That is a stunning dress you have on."

Lilly blushed and said a soft "Thank you. You are exceedingly kind."

"Fred, Lilly, here we are over here."

"Tony, Ariel, so good to see you." He nodded at the hostess, "You certainly arranged a warm welcome for us."

"Krystal is one of the best people in here. We've known her for several years, and she always treats us like royalty."

"Actually, Reverend Southgate, that's the way I think of you." She turned to the Livinggoods, "The Reverend helped me out of a difficult situation awhile back, and I'll never forget it. He didn't even know me back then, but he knew I was hurting, and he reached out. I started going to church again because that's what I think churches should do."

Tony reached out and squeezed Krystal's arm. "Maybe I'll have you give a testimonial someday."

"Me, speak in front of the church? I love you, Reverend, but that might be too much even for you. What will you fine folks have to drink?"

Soon they were all seated, and Ariel spoke to Krystal, "After you get their drink orders, please bring the appetizers we spoke about. Then shut the world out and allow us to have some fun."

Turning to back to the table, Ariel continued, "Lilly mentioned that she would like to taste some African food, so we took the liberty of ordering some special falafel for appetizers. After that, we can explore the menu and choose a variety that we can explore together. One of the reasons we like to come here is to taste the variety they offer from all over Africa."

"Fred, it is clear from what I'm hearing that a lot of your members are stirred up by your recent sermon." Tony reached out and placed a hand on Fred's arm. "I know about conflict, but my first concern is about you and Lilly. Ariel and I have known that pressure before, so tell us about how you are holding up. Then," he winked at his wife, "we'll start having some fun."

"Yeah, Mr. Thin Man," Lilly poked him in the arm, "tell the Southgates about all the Divine nudges you've been receiving lately."

Ariel's face took on a puzzled frown. "This I've got to hear," she said as she placed her cheek on her upraised palm and leaned in.

"I suppose there is a danger of reading God into each fortunate event," Fred began, "but the events of the last couple of weeks have seemed like God is reaching out to me in a special way. It's not been without pain and some rupture in relationships that I valued, but I have felt like I -- we--" he touched Lilly's shoulder, "are not alone in what we are experiencing."

"I assume that 'thin moments' are references to the Celtic concept?" said Tony. He turned to Ariel, "It's those experiences when you feel like the eternal is brushing up against your life, and you sense God's whisper."

Ariel selected a falafel and passed the plate to the Livinggoods. She even shivered a moment and said, "I love those God whispering moments; go on; I can't wait."

And for the next thirty minutes, Fred, occasionally supplemented by Lilly's contributions, related the several unexpected transforming moments that had taken place in the last week from five-year-old children to strange graffiti on the church wall and seemingly recalcitrant elders showing a surprising ability to listen.

"You've been through a lot, my brother, and I'm grateful for those spiritual moments that gave you courage."

Lilly spoke up, "We haven't been through what you two have. We haven't even asked about Eric. How is his recovery?"

"Thank the Lord," Ariel said, "he is a strong son. While it will take some time, the doctors are optimistic about his physical recovery. His mental recovery is another challenge. He's still pretty bitter about the incident."

"He's not the only one," said Tony. "I don't know how Jesus forgave those who mocked, beat, and crucified him. Every time we pray the Lord's Prayer and get to that forgiveness part, I feel guilty about my inability to be sincere. I say the words 'forgive us our debts -- or sins -- as we forgive those who sin against us,' but I'm not doing a particularly good job fulfilling my half of the bargain. Right now, I'm not especially good at offering forgiveness to the police who shot my son or many other racists who rip our society apart."

"It's hard to help our son get past those feelings," said Ariel, "when we can't get past them ourselves."

Fred raised his hand and signaled Krystal to come over. "Let's order our meal and another round of drinks. Then I want to share some ideas that have been floating around in my brain that speak to that very thing."

With Krystal's guidance, they ordered a series of dishes and some extra plates so they could each share a taste of all the different dishes.

When they completed their orders and Krystal had left to place the orders, Tony said, "Fred, Lilly, you were both there when we desperately needed you, and I am incredibly grateful. I don't want to spoil our evening by discussing solutions to 400 years of racism in this country that will not change. I've learned the hard way that you can swallow some hard feelings and put on a good face for the public. We can discuss that another time."

Krystal interrupted their conversation as she began placing plates on the table and explaining each dish she served. As she finished, she turned to Ariel and Tony. "Reverend, I heard about your son. If you tell me what hospital, I could visit him and bring him a special dish to cheer him up."

"That's so sweet, dear," Ariel said. "He's at Bradley Hospital, room 1506. I'm sure he would love some non-hospital food."

"You be careful as well, Krystal. It's dangerous out on these streets." He motioned to Fred and Lilly, "These are good folks, but there are a lot of crackers out there who are filled with a lot of prejudice and fear. It's like living in a foreign country where uniforms are a sign of danger, not safety."

As Krystal left to tend to other tables, Fred broke the momentary silence. "I want to have fun and relax tonight, too," he said, "but "I don't want to just avoid conversation about these struggles and what my congregation and I are called to do." Or "should do"? or "ought to be doing"? or…?

"Fred's right," Ariel said, "It's just that you can get so tired of always being alert to the enemy and their land mines everywhere. I've often thought that one of the reasons that lots of Black churches have so much shouting and dancing in their worship services is that it is a chance to blow off steam and release the tension."

"Okay," said Lilly, "here is a proposal. For the next forty-five minutes, we will focus on tasting these dishes, telling jokes, and maybe," she nodded towards Ariel, "even a few whoops and hollers. Then we'll get serious for the first of several conversations."

Tony raised and extended his open hands to be slapped by the others. "All right, sister." And turning to Fred, "How did you luck onto this Amazon princess?"

Grinning, Fred extended an arm to include both Lilly and Ariel, "Like you, some of us are just blessed in more ways than we deserve."

For the next forty-five minutes, they tasted and commented on the food, even occasionally calling Krystal over to explain about one of the dishes.

 **FOR CHAPTER RESOURCES AND ADDITIONAL CONTENT, SCAN THIS QR CODE:**
SMcCutchan.Kartra.com/page/CHAPTER17

# CHAPTER 18

# TRUTH AND RECONCILIATION

The meal was finished, and they sent Krystal off for a special dessert and coffee. Fred decided it was time to return to the topic of race and racism. "From what you have taught me and from what I've learned from reading several books, I think there are at least two levels that we need to discuss. I'm not sure that many White people understand that when we talk about racism, there is both the issue of personal racism and institutional racism."

"That's very important," said Tony, "but it gets even more complicated than that. We are both affected by racism, but we experience that cost very differently."

"Could we have some conversation among members of our two congregations where you could help us understand more about this?"

Tony glanced at Ariel and then back at Fred. "To be honest, Fred, your congregation probably needs to be willing to do a lot more work in preparation for such a conversation than most White congregations are willing to do. I'm not sure that would work very well. It wouldn't be fair to my congregation."

"I thought they would like that," said Lilly with a frown on her face.

"We've been through a lot of these discussions before," said Ariel. "It gets tiresome explaining the same thing over and over, and then nothing changes. If a White congregation did their homework first, then we could get into some real conversation and maybe even some effective ways to confront racism in the larger society."

"Right now, you are just confronting the fires from your rather blunt sermon," said Tony. "As your friend, I'll help you in any way that I can. But after numerous such conversations like this, many of my members are weary spending energy trying to help White people deal with their discomforts. At the same time, we continue to navigate the dangers of this society for our families and us. It's exhausting."

Everyone looked at each other. No one moved for a few moments, then Fred picked up his drink and extended it towards Tony and Ariel. "I don't think that was easy for you to say. Thank you for trusting us enough to be that honest. I'm not sure where to go with this or how to help my members to be willing to do their homework, but I'm grateful that you are willing to trust us enough to begin with some truth-telling."

"Go on and tell them what you were sharing with me about that eschuche thingy," said Lilly with a smile. "I'm not a theologian, but I think this was one of Fred's 'Pentecost moments' when he understood what God was saying in another language."

"Ha! This I've got to hear." Tony reached over and gave Ariel's hand a brief squeeze.

"It's not fleshed out yet, but it's an idea about how to engage my members in doing their homework. It begins with one of those 'thin moments' that happened the next day after the infamous sermon. I think I told you about the graffiti painted on the church and how one of the messages was painted by a different person from the rest? It simply said, 'Escúcheme, or 'Listen to me.' My Associate, Karen, and I have been playing with how we might use the Internet to help our members listen to each other about their feelings about racism and how it relates to the Gospel."

"Okay, I'll set my skepticism aside for a moment and open my ears. It would be mind-boggling if a White congregation began to wrestle with racism and the Gospel. If you can pull that off, we really would have some Good News to share."

"I'll share more detail as I develop it, but in a sketchy form, it looks like this. I want to make use of today's technology to engage the whole congregation in a conversation about our understanding of the church and God's call to us as a congregation."

Tony pulled out a couple of three by five cards and a pen, prepared to take notes. "I'm listening."

"We'd explain to every member, through email, letter, and newsletter, that -- like in the Pentecost experience described in Acts," Fred glanced playfully towards Lilly, "the members of our church come from a lot of different places and perspectives. We think it would be interesting to see if God can speak to us through what God has gathered together. Over the next couple of months, we are going to send out a series of questions to all the members. First, we'll offer a set of four possible answers, and each person is to choose the one they think best and respond within a few days. The fun part will be that we'll build a graph and show the congregation what this church looks like when we receive the responses. It won't be a vote, but just a picture of people's spontaneous feelings."

"Can you give me some samples of the questions?" Tony asked.

"Sure. It will begin with some light questions. If it works, we'll dig deeper, including eventually adding questions addressing our understanding of racism and the church.

Fred pulled out some paper from his coat. Here is a sample of the type of questions I'm talking about. He handed a sheet to each of them and laid one where Lilly could read it.

1. To lessen conflict and create harmony, pastors should:

    A. Avoid preaching on Scriptures that might be controversial.

    B. Only preach on subjects about which everyone agrees.

    C. Acknowledge potential disagreements about points made and encourage further conversation.

    D. Allow people to vote on which parts of the Gospel they like and preach accordingly.

2. Characteristics of a successful preacher are:

    A. Ability to preach sermons that inspire but don't offend.

    B. Preach sermons plainly grounded in the Bible.

    C. Preach with integrity even when it offends but is open to feedback.

    D. Preaches sermons that address personal issues but avoids commenting on social issues.

3. Cynicism and distrust are reduced in a congregation when:

    A. opinions are heard and respected.

    B. Controversial issues are not discussed.

    C. People accept that none of their views are perfect in God's eyes and continually seek to grow in understanding.

    D. People are committed to a shared vision of the church's mission.

"Fred, I like that. It's easy to respond to, and people will get excited about discovering how the whole church feels. In fact, it would be fun to try it in my church as well."

"It's also good," added Ariel, "that you begin by poking at the preacher. It will help them relax and have fun at it. Of course, if everyone chooses that the preacher should always preach sermons that don't offend, you two will be in trouble."

"As I think about it," said Tony, "even if that happened on some question, at least you would have the point of departure for a larger discussion. Also, I think when people see that boldly graphed out, it might also give them second thoughts as well."

Still looking at the questions, Tony continued, "And you say that after you worked through several questions to get them involved, you would then move deeper and get them to wrestle with faith and race?" Tony was writing notes rapidly, even as he talked.

"I don't have it all worked out yet, but that is my intention," said Fred. "Karen's been helping me both with developing the flow of the questions and with the technology that allows us to engage in conversation. She'll help develop visuals that allow us to build pictures of who we are."

"Okay, this opens up new territory. I think it is fresh and different enough that I might get my congregation to participate. What if each of us led our congregations through this?"

"And occasionally," said Ariel with growing excitement, "we could compare the graphs from each congregation. Our common experience is we are each in churches. Before they know it, we could all be hooked in, setting a little groundwork for talking about race and racism."

Fred felt a surge of energy. "We'd be educating ourselves and exploring possible new understandings. With the technology that is developing, maybe a little further down the road, both congregations could share the summaries of response from each of our churches.

"I've been thinking about this. How could we develop a deeper conversation that might lead to some positive activity addressing racism?"

"You have a fresh idea," Fred asked.

"I'm not sure, but here is an idea. How much do you know about the situation in South Africa and the Truth and Reconciliation Commission?"

"Not as much as I would like," Fred admitted, "but it was how that country dealt with race relations after Apartheid was over, wasn't it? That's what Desmond Tutu helped set up."

"Yes, the nation attempted to heal racial wounds and rebuild their society. Part of the reason our country has never been able to heal from its 'original sin' of racism, is that we have yet to have a real reckoning with the truth of our history. Some have been discussing how that process could be adapted to fit our culture and situation."

"You mean having our churches have their own version of a Truth and Reconciliation Commission," said Lilly.

"Wouldn't that be a trip if the path that heals racism in the states comes from Africa?, said Ariel."

"I think that is what's called 'poetic justice,' said Fred.

"I don't know if it can happen," said Tony, "but if we pursue the conversations that you propose, and in the process, our congregations developed some trust in each other, perhaps we could develop the courage to have our own Truth and Reconciliation experience?"

"Before we get too carried away," said Fred, "remember there is a major difference. If I understand what happened in South Africa, there had been a real shift in power, and the question was whether that would result in a real blood bath as the new powerholders sought revenge for how they were treated. There hasn't been that shift in power here."

"Hey, you are catching on," said Tony as a smile crossed his face. "The real issue about racism, as opposed to prejudice and bigotry, is the issue of power. In South Africa, those who came before the Commission represented two different experiences. There were the Blacks who had suffered horribly under the old system, and the Whites, who had taken actions that had caused those sufferings. The challenge was whether the new regime would seek vengeful justice or restorative justice."

"So how do we balance the power issue in our church commission?" said Fred.

"Wait a minute, folks," Lilly ventured. "I have listened to my husband preach about suffering servants, how God always starts small, and how we all need to be captured by a vision if we will keep marching across the wilderness. We've got some time to think about this while we try the first step, but doesn't the foundation of our faith provide us with principles to guide us? Maybe God can show us the next step if we keep our eyes on the prize."

Tony dropped his pen on the table, shoved back his chair, and stood up. "Lilly, you have Fred and Ariel to protect your virtue, but you are about to get a big hug from a grateful man who has experienced truth spilling out of your lips."

"I think she is going to get a big hug from all three of us!" announced Ariel. "That was beautifully said, Lilly. My faith, hope, and love have been revived this evening. I'm closest, so I get to hug you first." She moved quickly around the table and enveloped Lilly in her arms.

A slightly flustered but pleased Lilly was soon enveloped by all three of them.

At that moment, Krystal came up to their table. "I'm not sure what is going on here, but I was going to ask if anyone wanted anything more to eat or drink?"

"I was going to ask for coffee," said Fred, "but I think a small glass of champagne for each of us might be appropriate."

Krystal grinned and said, "Is it appropriate for me to ask what you are celebrating?"

"Just the first step in bringing healing and hope to our city and maybe beyond," said Tony.

**FOR CHAPTER RESOURCES
AND ADDITIONAL CONTENT,
SCAN THIS QR CODE:**

SMcCutchan.Kartra.com/page/CHAPTER18

# CHAPTER 19

# AN UNCERTAIN VISION

Karen greeted Fred in the hallway as he entered the church on Thursday morning. She had a big grin on her face. "Now comes the real work," Karen said. "As you know, I sent out the first group of questions that we agreed upon on Sunday evening and set Wednesday as a deadline. We've got a great response. I'll bet we set a record. Whoever heard of a congregation being asked a question and getting an 80% response?"

"Eighty percent? That is fantastic! What happened?"

"Fred, you struck a home run in that sermon of yours. People wander around this society, wondering who is in charge and, more importantly, whether anyone is listening, let alone gives a hoot about what they are thinking. Most of them also feel guilty about their faith. They come to church hoping that somehow they might hear a whisper from above about what life is really about. Maybe it won't last, but just for a moment, they began thinking that maybe God is real and does expect something from this church."

Karen continued as she motioned Fred over to see some printouts on her desk. "Let me show you a graph of their responses to the first set of questions. You asked what their opinion was about how to nurture a warm, welcoming church. Their response was fascinating. Look at this pie chart."

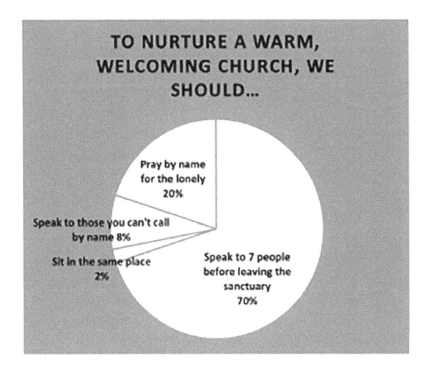

"That alone should stimulate an awareness of the need to seek out and speak to others actively," mused Fred.

"And you will love this one, Fred. When asked how you can know you can trust our pastor, their response was:

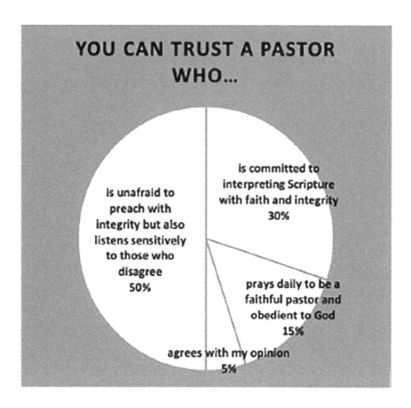

"Isn't that fascinating?" Karen quizzed. "Next steps, I plan to graph those results and send them back out to the congregation. I'll tell them that other questions will follow, but that first we are interested in feedback of no more than three sentences interpreting what they hear from these first two responses. I'm curious if members feel we might have some fun with this as a congregation. As we send out more questions, we can let Fran and her crew begin to combine the responses into a collective image we are building of the congregation."

"I've got some other good news for you. Lilly and I had supper with the Southgates, and a couple of things came up that I think hold real promise. Have you got a few minutes for me to tell you about it?"

"Another one of those 'thin moments' you are always experiencing?" she probed and giggled softly.

"Maybe," Fred said as he invited her to sit in a chair in his office. "It certainly has possibilities."

"Fred, I may be a little cynical about too quickly claiming a message from God, but you've had too many of these 'accidental and might not have been' moments not to make me pay attention when you think you've had another one."

"I've never heard it described that way before, but I like it."

Karen settled in her seat. "In fact, given the recent events and people's response to these first questions, I'm even eager to see what you are thinking about. However," she held up her hand, "might I get you a cup of coffee first, just in case exploring this takes more than a few minutes?"

"If you won't tell anyone that I let my female Associate serve me coffee rather than the other way around, that would be very nice."

"Don't worry; your masculine chauvinism will be our little secret."

When Karen returned with two steaming cups of coffee and some cream and sugar, Fred had already set up a whiteboard and began to sketch a few boxes. "You and I had briefly talked about how we would like to engage in some interaction between our congregation and Tony's. When I shared that idea with Tony, he did his best to be polite but declined. His basic message was that while he would help us any way he can, his people have been down the road of educating White people too many times, and they were tired of all words and no action."

"Actually," said Karen. "when you think about it, that's understandable. I recently read a book, Good White Racists, I think, and they were making the same point. It's a little naive to think we just need to sit down and talk about the love of neighbor and expect the problem to be resolved."

"But wait till you hear this. When I explained to Tony what you and I were planning, he began to get excited. He even turned to Ariel and commented, 'Wouldn't it be fun to see how our congregation would answer those same questions?'

"Then," Fred continued, "and this is where it gets even more exciting, he has been reading about the Truth and Reconciliation Commission in South Africa. He was wondering whether that could ever happen within individual churches in the U.S. We both knew there would have to be a lot of adaptions, but the idea is tantalizing."

"I don't know much about the Commission, but I do remember it structured some painful but candid sessions between the races. It fits into the discipline of Active Listening that you mentioned. I'm not sure, however, that our nation is interested in really listening to each other right now."

"I agree, but what do you think would be the impact if a Black and a White church could demonstrate the possibility of that in our society?"

"To quote a recent sermon I've heard, we might be able to paint an image of a promised land where diverse people could be enriched rather than separated by their differences."

"It's exciting to think about, but first we have to figure out how we get this congregation to learn how to even listen to each other and see where that takes us."

Karen set her cup down and patted her lips. "My news is not so exciting as that, but Ezekiel and I were playing online the other night. I think a rather clever idea began to emerge. While we want to engage the membership in a congregation-wide conversation, the challenge is to get them all to participate, not only once, as they have, but to continue as it gets even more complex and serious."

"Yeah, I've watched people get bored rather fast when we've tried to introduce something new before."

"And your novel approach with the pre-designed questions will help, but what if we could introduce even more of a game-like quality that keeps them entertained?"

"Say more."

"I have to investigate it more, but there is a process on Survey Monkey that introduces a game-like experience to online interaction without losing the quality of the exchange. I will investigate more, but I think part of it introduces immediate feedback in the form of live graphs and charts that provide visuals as we develop the church's responses."

"It would be fascinating to develop an image of our current church and share it with Tony's church. Then together, we could build an image of the Promised Land that we can spread across our Presbytery or even ecumenically."

"Even more than that. I've gotten to know Fran a little bit more, and she is familiar with computer technology, so she can help us shape this."

Fred clapped his hands together. "My head is beginning to spin with possibilities! She and two or three of her friends are doing this as part of a class, aren't they?"

"Right, and – just think! -- if we had a mind-blowing success with this, what are universities more interested in than anything else?" Karen asked with a gleam in her eye.

"Publishing a breakthrough article that not only shows how forward-thinking they are but also makes them attractive to both new bright students and grants to fund exciting research."

"Boy, that is dreaming, isn't it? But it is true that when an exciting vision grasps you, it does fill you with energy!"

Fred grabbed a notebook and stood up. "So, we need to do a couple of things. We need to engage our current membership in a conversation that they find both interesting and fun. Let's explore what type of programs Survey Monkey offers us. We can start building a picture of the current membership and its diversity.

"Then, having identified its essential characteristics--what attracted them to this church, how long they've been a member, age group, gender, etc., we will move on to some faith questions--God, Jesus, salvation, love of neighbor, church, etc. And perhaps we can add in there what questions they would like explored in more depth.

"Third, we can explore the area of corporate ministry -- what they affirm is vital that we do together as a church --worship, educate, fellowship, ministry to the community…

"Perhaps we can also identify the areas of concern that they would like to see the church address -- care for the vulnerable, feed the hungry, address the needs of children, counseling for people who are struggling…" Fred was out of breath.

"We might challenge them to identify what they think Jesus would ask of this church in addressing these problems," said Karen. "And as we get into this, we can introduce the issue of race and racism. And perhaps we can introduce the issue of the church's witness to the community. For example, we might begin to explore how the community is going to interpret our actions."

Fred continued to take notes. "At some point down the road, when we have people involved and interested in seeing the summaries of our responses, we can introduce the idea of sharing our conclusions with another church. If Tony's church is going through a similar process, we'll both be ready to exchange our church images. That would be our first introduction to our version of the Truth and Reconciliation Commission.  By sharing our corporate images and discussing the similarities and differences, we can begin to identify the areas where we need some deep Active Listening."

"Okay, let's both put together some follow up questions to

begin the process," Suggested Karen. "And let's bring Fran into it from the beginning. Her perspective as both an outsider and a young person might be refreshing. Besides, she can do it as part of her schoolwork, leading up to that mind-shattering article she is going to publish."

**FOR CHAPTER RESOURCES AND ADDITIONAL CONTENT, SCAN THIS QR CODE:**
SMcCutchan.Kartra.com/page/CHAPTER19

# CHAPTER 20

# ENGAGING THE CONGREGATION

Fred called a meeting of his task force on Saturday to discuss the follow-up. Victor and David greeted Fran and Karen warmly as they entered the conference room. They saw Fred, who was already setting out coffee cups and boxes of donuts on the table. Charles, the stated clerk, and Dianna were already in the room, chatting and munching on a donut.

"I assume you got a decent response to your first round of questions you sent out to the congregation?" Victor inquired as he selected a cream-filled, chocolate-covered donut and took a seat. "Um, good. Don't tell my wife how much I enjoyed this."

Karen passed around a paper containing the graphs of the first two questions. "Poll takers would drool over the percentages of our response -- Over 80% return within three days!"

"That's fantastic. The questions were equally non-threatening and almost playful," David chuckled as he glanced at the chart. "Nice way to prepare the groundwork with that question about pastors and sermons."

"Thank you, Victor," replied Karen. "The idea is to gently organize the flow of the questions as we move deeper. On the flip side of the handout, you'll find some other suggested questions. You will notice the flow moves towards faith questions, even before we begin to explore topics related to racism. "If the task force agrees we will begin to send them out two or three questions at a time and provide a report to the congregation as we get results."

"As you look at them," said Fred, "you might jot down your guess in percentages as to the response we will get."

Each of them took out their pens and chuckled a little as they began to sip their coffee and make their guesses as to the congregational response.

1. The biggest contributor to distrust among church members is:
    A. Inadequate communication.
    B. Feeling that only a few people make all the decisions.
    C. Not understanding how decisions are made in the church.
    D. Not holding a shared vision about the nature and mission of the church.

2. Cynicism and distrust are reduced in a congregation when:
    A. Diverse opinions are heard and respected.
    B. Controversial issues are not discussed.
    C. People accept that none of their opinions are perfect in God's eyes and continually seek to grow in understanding.
    D. People are committed to a shared vision of the church's mission.

3. The primary reason churches split is:
    A. Refusing to accept that we are all sinners and need to

forgive each other continually.

B. Choosing to emphasize right beliefs over loving behavior.

C. Refusing to accept as priority Jesus' command that we be one.

D. Allowing personal beliefs to take precedence over being faithful to the church.

4. Loving your enemy is most difficult when:

A. Your enemy is from a different culture.

B. Your enemy belongs to your church but has different beliefs.

C. Your enemy treats you with contempt.

D. Your enemy affirms a different faith.

5. The hardest part of the Lord's Prayer to accept is:

A. That God's will be done on earth.

B. That God will provide our daily bread, and we need not succumb to greed.

C. That God's forgiving us of our sins is affected by our willingness to forgive the sins of our neighbor.

D. That God's not leading us into temptation will contribute to God's delivering us from evil.

"I don't know which of you came up with these," said Victor, "but there is a little bit of devil in you with these last two questions. I think in business polling, that's called 'push polling.' The way the question is framed pushes the respondent into thinking in a new direction." He smiled. "I don't object. It's where we need to go. I think the results will be fascinating."

"It hadn't occurred to me earlier," said Dianna, "but as I was filling in my guesses, I kept wondering how different members would fill theirs out. What if we asked them to keep a copy of the questions and make their personal guesses as to the overall congregational response."

"That's brilliant, Dianna. That way, it almost becomes a game, and people will be less anxious and want to see how correct they were." Said Karen, "Maybe you should offer a small prize for those who made the best guesses to keep up the fun. You know, maybe a $5 gift certificate to Starbucks or something like that."

"I'm assuming," said Charles, "that as you proceed, the questions will get a little more sensitive and challenging. Maybe by the time they get them, they will already be in a game mode and more willing to participate."

"I think that might work," exclaimed Karen. "If we can get the congregation fully involved, there is another stage that Fred came up with that can up the ante a little. Tell them what Tony said, Fred."

"Well, this is still in the early planning stages," said Fred, "but you remember the warm response Tony got at last week's service?" They all nodded, and Fred continued, "Well, when I was telling him what we were planning, he suggested that it might be fun to see if his congregation would go through the same process. At some point, we could share the respective church images we are fleshing out."

"We'd have to be careful how we begin talking about race, but if we could move past the initial hesitancy," mused Charles, "we might be able to get to an in-depth conversation. Were you thinking about sharing via the Internet, or can we have some joint potluck suppers or something like that?"

"Frankly, I don't know," said Fred, "and I would have to consult with Tony about any plans like that. It would put an interesting spin on what we are doing if we could pull that off."

Fran, who had slipped in quietly and was listening from a corner, raised her hand hesitantly.

Fred called on her. "I think you all know Fran, who, along with some colleagues, has volunteered to assist us as part of a course she is taking. If it all works, they may even write it up in a paper she's preparing. Feel free to chime in, Fran. "

"First, let me say I'm enjoying working with Fred and Karen on the technology side of this. Second, if this is moving in the right direction, I'd also be willing to help with the technology that can help the congregation have an entire congregation conversation. And some of my classmates would be willing to help the other congregation to converse as well. If you do decide on some virtual conversations, we are pretty familiar with that technology."

"Tony had expressed to me," said Fred, "that many of his congregation might be hesitant to speak too openly in front of a large body of White members. As Fran was speaking, it occurred to me that we might be able to build some trust by having some of the first joint meetings be on shared videotapes. If we are going to get into depth, this might be a safe way to begin."

"At least early on, that might be a good way to start. This will be new territory for many of our members, and I wouldn't want some insensitive remarks to torpedo our efforts early on," said David. "Can you share with us some of the questions you're considering for the next phase of this process?"

"We haven't got that far yet. I'd want to work those out with Tony to make sure we are all on the same page," said Fred.

"The idea of sharing on some videos sounds like a good idea," said Jerry. "I'm beginning to both get excited and nervous all at the same time."

"What is our end goal in all this?" Victor asked.

"That is an excellent question, Victor." Fred looked around at all those present. "I can give you a partial answer, but it may seem way too idealistic. We do need to have a clearer idea of our endgame. After I try to describe my ideas, I'd like each of you to respond with ideas of your own." They looked at him and waited on his next words. "In a global sense, I believe that the racial tension in our community and our country is not only wrong for our country but is in contradiction to the Gospel. I doubt if any of you would disagree with that. However, and this is where we may have some legitimate disagreements, I think God may call us as a church to act in ways that challenge racism in our own lives and our church and maybe even act out that faith in our society." People began to shift in their seats as if they were planning to respond. Fred held up his hand. "I love our church, and I don't want to do anything that would harm or split our community. I know that is a risk in our current situation."

"That's certainly my concern," interjected David.

"But," Fred continued, "I also believe in God. I don't want to lead our church in defying what the Gospel asks of us. I know you don't either, so we have to step carefully. But we can't let our fear of conflict cause us to choose peace at the cost of denying our faith."

"And you think asking these questions is going to help us hear God?" Dianna asked.

"I'm hoping that if we can engage the whole congregation -- or at least most of them -- in exploring these questions together," said Fred, "we'll see that no one of us has the definite answer. But as we genuinely try to listen to each other, God may help us come to some new understandings that will not only deepen our faith but be good for our society as well."

"You all know that I strongly disagreed with Fred when he called us all racists in that famous sermon," said Victor. "However, since then, I've come to see Fred's sincerity and his love for this church. I am willing to go along with him, at least for a while, and see if we can't grow stronger as a church if we dare to listen more than we spout off. I'm rather intrigued to see where this question thing will go."

"I see value in helping us all talk with each other," said David. "Help me understand how this will help ease the racial tension in our society?"

Fred nodded as he thought for a moment. "Here's my thinking. First, if a church can own our differences but still listen to and support each other, I think that alone demonstrates a way of relating to each other that the world seems to have forgotten lately. Jesus said in one Beatitude, 'Blessed are the Peacemakers, for they shall be called children of God.' What does it mean to take this Beatitude seriously?"

"Dang," said David, "I hate it when he begins to make sense. Especially when it's going to cost me something."

Several chuckled and nodded their heads.

"But we also have a developing relationship with Tony Southgate's church. What if a community of White Christians could genuinely listen to and speak with a community of Black Christians and seek how to heal the racial divisions in our society? I don't know if we can do that, but I am certain it won't happen unless we try. I also believe that is what Jesus wants us to do."

Victor turned towards Martha, the only Black member of the Session. "What do you think, Carolyn? Would something like that work in a Black church?"

There was an audible sigh from Fran, who was sitting in the corner.

Carolyn sat up a little straighter and faced Victor. "First of all, Victor, I don't speak for all Black people, Christian or otherwise. Second, last time I checked, not all Black churches are the same. It isn't only White churches that have a diverse membership."

"I apologize, Martha. I shouldn't have asked it that way. There is a lot of subtlety in this subject of racism. I'm beginning to think Fred is closer to the truth than I realized."

"What I think Fred is both risking and trusting," said Carolyn with a smile, "is that this congregation is teachable. I believe you are strong enough to learn from your mistakes, but I'm not as sure about the whole congregation. I joined this congregation because I thought it was open-minded. Overall, I've been pleased, but there have been plenty of times when I've just had to breathe deeply and swallow what I was feeling."

Suddenly the conference room door opened, and Alice peeked into the room. "I'm sorry to interrupt, but Reverend Southgate is on the phone and says it is an emergency."

Fred jumped up, turned to Karen, and said, "You can moderate this conversation, and I will go to see what Tony wants." He quickly left the room.

"I think we are demonstrating right here what can happen when people who aren't afraid to speak their true feelings also are willing to make a genuine effort to listen to each other. I don't know whether it is God speaking, but I do sense a glimmer of hope that something good can emerge if we can continue this journey faithfully," reflected Dianna.

**FOR CHAPTER RESOURCES
AND ADDITIONAL CONTENT,
SCAN THIS QR CODE:**
SMcCutchan.Kartra.com/page/CHAPTER20

# CHAPTER 21

# TAKING A HOSTAGE

Fred grabbed the phone in his office. "Tony, what's going on?"

"Krystal, from the restaurant, just called. She was headed home and stopped by our local Jimmy's Mini Mart to get some aspirin and something to drink. As she chose her drink, a Black man burst into the story ranting about a racist society, pulling a gun and threatening to shoot anyone who moved."

"How'd she get to call you?"

"She's originally from Uganda and isn't easily cowed by tough situations. She told the man that she understood what he was talking about but didn't want anyone to get hurt. Then she told him she knew two preachers she trusted that could help if he would let her call them."

The clerk had already pushed the emergency button under the counter, and they could hear the sirens of the approaching police. There were about ten people in the store, and he had gathered them near the counter. He told her to go ahead and call her prissy preachers, but if the police tried to come into the store, a lot of people were going to get hurt."

Fred signaled Alice to come to his office, telling Tony he would meet him at the Jimmy's Mini Mart in about ten minutes. When Alice opened the office door, he said, "Alice, there is a hostage situation over at the Jimmy's Mini Mart, and Tony thinks we can be of help. I'm leaving now and want you to call Lilly; tell her what I've told you and that I'll call her as soon as possible, but I can't promise when I'll be home. Then, tell Karen and the group the same story and that they should go ahead and wrap things up, go home, and wait till I can tell them more."

"Will do, and we will all be in prayer for you. Do be as careful as you can be."

Fred ran out of the door and jumped into his car to speed towards the store.

He arrived in less than ten minutes and saw that the police were already surrounding the parking lot, halting any traffic from getting near. One officer, who turned out to be Phil Glazer-- the same officer who had checked out the graffiti at the church a few weeks ago -- approached the car. "Reverend Livinggood, if I recall correctly."

"That's right. How are things unfolding here?"

"Not good, but they are expecting you. Reverend Southgate will meet you at the door. Be careful, sir. The man inside is crazy unhinged."

"Thanks, officer." Fred left his car and approached Tony, who was standing by the store door.

"Thanks for coming. Fred. Krystal is waiting to let us in. From then on, we wing it."

Fred and Tony entered the store and saw a frightened group of people crowded together off to the left of a tall, middle-aged Black man who held both a pistol and a shotgun in his hands.

"Nice of these stores to supply their racist clerks with shotguns. It makes it easier for me to do real damage."

He waved the guns to indicate that they should approach. "Young lady, you join the others. You've done your part. Now it's time for your preacher friends."

Krystal didn't appear as nervous as the others. "I'll join them, but let me introduce you to Reverend Southgate, pastor of Mt. Sinai, and Reverend Fred Livinggood of Fourth Presbyterian.

"You may call me Tony, and what shall we call you?"

"Guess it don't make any difference anyway. I'll probably never leave this place alive. You can call me Tyler Fishermen. And what's your name?" He pointed the shotgun toward Fred.

"Call me Fred. Can you tell Tony and me what happened that led up to this?"

"I'll tell you what happened. I've finally taken all the racist bullshit I can take. Today was the last straw."

"What happened today?" Tony asked.

"Well, first, I tried to tell my dumb-ass supervisor about something he was doing wrong. He got pissed off letting a Black man tell him what's wrong. We got into an argument, and he told me that if I got all uppity again, he'd fire me.

"Uppity! I'd been bowing and scraping and kissing his ass for over a year. I told him he could take his job and shove it up where the sun don't shine. I needed that job to support my wife and kids, but I couldn't take it anymore."

"So, you felt that he was a racist and not treating you fairly,"

Fred said. "And he was so prejudiced that he couldn't even listen to fair criticism that would have helped him correct what he was doing wrong."

"That's right. Blacks in that factory always have to do the shit work, and then you have to put up with a bunch of mealy-mouthed crackers who don't know what they are doing trying to lord it all over you.

"You felt from the beginning that Blacks got the raw end of the deal and weren't given real respect even though they did most of the work that kept the factory productive." Fred paused and waited.

"It just ain't fair. And then, when you leave the factory, it starts all over again out in the bigger world. You should know," he pointed at Tony. "I'll bet even though you're a preacher that people are always trying to humiliate you and hurt your family."

"They have hurt his family, and it wasn't fair for them either."

Tyler turned to look at Tony, who replied, "Three weeks ago, the police in the neighborhood six blocks over shot my son. He'll live, but I'm still angry about what shouldn't have happened."

"I'm sorry, but none of this shit should happen. It happens right here in this store. This pasty-faced clerk is always sassing my wife and treating her with disrespect -- commenting about her ass or implying that she may be hiding extra products in her purse. She does carry a big purse, but she would never lift anything -- hell, I may not be a good man, but she is a faithful church woman."

"In addition to trouble at the factory, you have to endure the racism in our society. And when you can't even protect your wife, it makes you feel less than a man," Tony said. "I've been there. I'll bet your kids have experienced it as well."

"One time, my daughter was kicked out of this store because they said she was spending too much time reading the magazines. And my son was pulled over by the police last month for driving while Black." He turned to Fred. "Have you got kids?"

Fred nodded. "I have two kids."

"Let me ask you something. I'll bet the Reverend here knows what I'm talking about. Have you ever had The Talk with your kids about where to put your hands and how to act when stopped by the police?"

"No, the worst I've had to do is support her when other kids at school picked on her for being a Preacher's Kid. It's bad but nowhere near what you're talking about."

Fred was aware of two changes in the atmosphere in the store. First, the bystanders listened with interest to the conversation that he, Tony, and Tyler were having. Their bodies weren't as tense, almost like they had forgotten what was happening. And second, although Tyler was still alert and holding his guns ready, he was less tense as he realized someone was willing to listen to what was bothering him.

"It just gets so exhausting dealing with these crackers and all their rules and prejudices all the time. You never can relax and just enjoy life. And it's not right that people think they can all speak dirty to my wife; plus, if I try to do anything about it, they throw my ass in jail. I have blood pressure problems and nervous thoughts on my best days, and I don't have too many of them anymore."

"I think you got a right to be angry and pissed off with all you have to put up with," said Fred.

"I agree," said Tony, "but I don't want you to hurt your family by doing something crazy that a bunch of honkies can use to blame you for the violence and law-breaking in our society."

"My goose is already cooked. They ain't never going to let me go after this."

"I think they will arrest you," said Fred, "but I can assure you that those news cameras out there are going to hear the real story about why you did what you did and the courage that you showed in exposing the injustice that the average Black person has to put up with every day. Your family can be proud rather than ashamed of who you are, and Tony and I will work hard to build up sympathy that can result in a lighter sentence for you."

Tyler stared at Tony and Fred. And then the guns that were in his hands began to shake. He stepped towards them and, guns in his hands, threw his arms around them and began to weep.

A strange thing began to happen. It started with one young lady from the group of hostages who stepped toward them. "Tyler," she whispered. He lifted his head and looked at her as she continued, "You scared the bejeebers out of me, but hearing what you have been through makes me deeply ashamed of my society. I don't know what they will do to you, but I promise you that if there is a trial, I'll be there. I will testify on your behalf."

Then slowly, several other patrons stepped forward and repeated similar messages.

A couple of the people began to protest and declare that he had no right to endanger their lives that way, but as they did, others challenged them. "Of course, it was wrong, but if you had been treated so wrong and your family humiliated like he was, how long would you have lasted? He risked our lives, but now he has laid his life on the line. He'll suffer for our sake. What are we willing to do for his sake?"

"Are you ready for us to open the door and let the police in, Tyler?" Tony asked.

He nodded, and Krystal moved towards the door to let the police in. There was some befuddlement on the faces of the officers when, as they proceeded to cuff Tyler, the hostages began to clap and cheer for their captor.

Soon the television cameras were whirring, and the newscasters were crowding in with their questions. Fred decided it was a good time to step in and take charge.

"If you will all quiet down and gather around, I think we have some statements to make, and then we will take your questions. I suspect that after the Reverend Southgate and I have made our statements, several of the people taken hostage will be open to your questions as well."

"What did you do to disarm the shooter?" one of the reporters shouted.

Tony spoke, "First, we didn't disarm the shooter. He chose to lay down his guns. What we did can be summed up in one word I first heard from Reverend Livinggood. It is Escúcheme. I'll translate that for you so you won't have to scramble through your Spanish dictionary. It means 'Listen to me!' What we did for Tyler -- which is the name of the human that you are calling 'the shooter' -- What we did was listen to him; and he, in turn, listened to us. Too much of the violence in our society results from our failure to listen to each other. As Dr. Martin Luther King, Jr. said, 'A riot is the language of the unheard.' This was not a riot, but as you will learn when you hear Tyler's story, his threat of violence was his language for crying out and saying, 'listen to me -- not only for himself but also for his wife and children. They have all suffered from the sometimes unconscious and sometimes conscious racism of our society. I'm not in any way justifying Tyler's actions, but I am saying that when Fred and I genuinely tried to listen to him -- not just to his words but to his pain, he felt free to lay down his weapons."

Fred picked up from Tony. "This requires a lot more time to explain than we have time for, but it is a dramatic example of what each of us should already know. When we are treated with contempt and degraded as subhuman not only by individuals but by society as a whole, it rubs our nerves raw. And at times, as it did for Tyler, your emotions explode. It was an irrational act, which I think Tyler will now admit, but it could have been avoided if humans had treated humans with enough compassion to listen to each other.

"We have a long way to go with this, but let us allow the

courage of Tyler Fishermen to be part of the spark that ignites a more compassionate world. Fourth Presbyterian and Mt. Sinai Presbyterian are both going to try to deepen our ministry to those who are wounded by society. I would encourage all of you to do the same."

The interviews went on for a while. Soon Fred and Tony redirected the reporters' interest to those who had been held hostage. The reporters were fascinated and hungry for details about the hostages who had turned into advocates for their captor.

Immediately when Fred could break away from the crowd and get in his car, he called Lilly to assure her he was all right.

"No one prepared me for this side of being a pastor's wife," she said. "You expect those types of things to happen to police or firemen -- not preachers. I'm grateful that Foster and Bridget could come and support me. Foster knows more about prayer than I ever imagined. He even got us on our knees a couple of times."

"I'm sorry, Lil. But I'm all right now and will be home in a few minutes."

"The way things have been happening lately, I think I'll believe that when I see you turn into the driveway. Who knows? Aliens from outer space could sweep in before you get here."

"Okay, if they do, I'll make them promise to stop by and pick you up before we leave the planet." He chuckled and hung up.

When Fred arrived home, Lilly, Foster, and Bridget came streaming out of the house, enveloping him in a gigantic group hug. It was the end of a very exhausting day, but seeing his family gave him a deep feeling of shalom, and he was incredibly grateful.

**FOR CHAPTER RESOURCES
AND ADDITIONAL CONTENT,
SCAN THIS QR CODE:**
SMcCutchan.Kartra.com/page/CHAPTER21

# CHAPTER 22

# LEADERS ARE SERVANTS

Fred had arranged with Karen and Fran to meet a week later before the morning services. "OK, let's review where we are," said Fred as he, Karen, and Fran gathered.

Karen opened her briefcase and brought out a package of papers. "I think this is getting exciting. Thanks to all that newspaper and TV coverage from your Jimmy's Mini Mart adventure, we have our whole congregation participating in this conversation, and the city waits with anticipation to see how Fourth Presbyterian will paint their image as a church."

"That was fantastic," said Fran. "I've gotten to know you well enough to understand that neither you nor Tony is in this for the publicity, but what you did was incredible. My classmates keep asking me if I can get some selfies and your autographs."

"I think we can skip that part," said Fred looking somewhat embarrassed.

"Oh, come on," said Karen as she whipped out her cell phone from her purse. "Given what Fran is doing for us, it's the least we can do. Come on, Fran, let's get on either side of our new superhero." Both Fran and Karen crowded on either side of Fred, and Karen snapped a couple of pictures. "We'll get the autographs later when we can also get a picture of Tony."

Fred picked up some of the papers that Karen had laid on the table. "Did you write this summary, Fran? That is well done."

"Karen gave me the graphs and some of the comment sheets from your first three sets of questions, and it sort of fell into place. I was impressed by what this says about the congregation. You may want to change this later, but I wrote it as a personal document that shares what I heard as I reviewed the response sheets." Fran looked a little sheepish and uncertain as she took her article out of her briefcase. "Maybe it would be best if I read it aloud to you first. Then I have copies, and we could critique it."

"I think that's an excellent idea, Fran. Let me fill our cups with coffee, and then we are all ears." When Fred had filled all their cups with coffee, he sat down and waved his hand towards Fran. "It's your show."

Fran shifted in her chair, laid her paper in front of her, cleared her throat, and began.

## A SUMMARY OF THE VIEWS OF THE MEMBERS OF FOURTH PRESBYTERIAN
PREPARED BY FRAN SMITH, of CITY COMMUNITY COLLEGE

My name is Fran Smith. I've been attending Fourth Presbyterian for about six months now and am a student at the   Community College. I'm taking a class on community building. Your pastors invited me to collect your votes for the questions and write a summary of the results.

My first conclusion in collecting the votes is that you are a wonderfully diverse congregation with strong opinions about various subjects. At the same time, it is clear that you value this church's warm and stimulating community and respect one another even when you disagree. Sixty-five percent emphasized the importance of listening to and respecting each other and recognizing that none of us are perfect and can learn from each other. If I were to pick three characteristics that expresses what is important to you as a group, they would be communication, the sense of family, and openness to feedback, especially when wrestling with controversial issues.

In addition to the obvious advantage of living near the church and having friends who were members, many of you shared that you were attracted to this church by the quality of worship, including the music and the honest wrestling with how faith speaks to real issues in this society rather than a rigid adherence to easy answers or simplistic doctrines.

Though you have differing opinions about the church's nature, you value a flexible but shared understanding of the faith that binds you together, and you wish to offer ministry that seeks to heal the brokenness in our world.

You support your pastors and value their integrity while expecting them to listen to members sensitively, especially when they disagree. To use the word your pastors have recently been quoting from the graffiti painted on the wall, escúcheme (or listen to me) sums up this congregation. When you practice it both ways, you have powerful

Good News to share with our world.

I wasn't reared in any church. I came here by accident when a boy I liked invited me to your youth group. As I look back on the events that led me to you a couple of years ago, I am reminded of what Pastor Fred calls a "thin moment" when I heard a whisper that has opened my heart. Thank you for being there for me and welcoming me in such a friendly and supportive way. In your own way, many of you did escúcheme, and I did hear God's whisper.

P.S.: The response sheets from which I wrote this article are available in the church office. We will continue to have more questions and conversation, which I will read with interest and attempt to summarize for you with integrity.

With love,

Fran Smith

"Okay, that's it," Fran said as she laid the papers on the desk and looked at them.

Karen was trying to wipe a tear from her eyes.

Fred also was having trouble deciding how to respond. "Fran, that is fabulous. Not only do I think you have captured what was expressed in the votes, but you did it in such a beautifully personal way that the article carries the power to touch anyone who reads it. Thank you. From the bottom of my heart, thank you."

Karen got up from the table and came around to where Fran was sitting. "Please get up and let me give you a big hug."

"Karen and I joked a few weeks ago when you volunteered for this task that we might even get written up in a college journal. I don't think we should wait for the end of the project," Fred said. "Ever since that Jimmy's Mini Mart incident, the reporters have sought an update. How would you feel if we shared your article with them and the congregation?"

"OK, if you think it's all right," she said.

"We have some other news," said Karen.

Fred spoke up. "Tony has expressed an interest in having his congregation answer a similar set of questions and then sharing the results with both of our congregations."

"How about another class member asking Reverend Southgate if he can be that church's reporter and summarize their results?" suggested Fran.

"That would be great. I'll talk to Tony about it. I'm going to meet with him tomorrow. I'll share what we've done so far and see where it goes. With all the publicity over that store incident, I don't think he'll have any problem getting participation in this first phase," said Fred.

"Then, working together," said Karen, "we can develop some questions on race and see if we could build enough relationship that we might venture into some version of the Truth and Reconciliation process."

"That would be cool. Just imagine what would happen if society could learn how to face our differences and learn from each other."

Karen slapped her hand on the table. "What a revolutionary idea! That churches could learn to listen to the truth and be committed to be reconciled to each other!" She paused, grinned, and continued,

"Oh wait, I think Jesus already said something like that. Who knew?"

"And in case you are wondering," added Fran, "even though our class will be ending soon, three of us want to continue on this project. We talked to some professors who are excited and willing to help us, so we are good to go on this end."

"Here we go again with all the unexpected events that move us along," said Karen. "Do you suppose it happened like that in the wilderness journey?"

"Does make you feel like you are part of something bigger than what we realized," said Fred.

"Okay, I'm becoming a believer," said Karen. "I think I'm beginning to hear whispers myself."

"What are you talking about?" quizzed Fran with a puzzled look on her face.

"I'll explain this deep theological mystery later," said Karen. "For now, we need to think about where we go from here."

"I think we need to talk to Tony," said Fred. "I think all the publicity around the event mentioned above at the Jimmy's Mini Mart moves our calendar of events up considerably. Karen, why don't you share some of the questions we have sketched out as a beginning."

Karen went to her office to print out a set of questions she had drafted for the next phase of the survey project.

"As you will see, Fran, we are following the same format of a statement or question with four possible responses from which to choose. We hope that both Black and White members will feel less exposed by this format. As you have seen in the first phase, it is also easier to graph the results that way." Fred paused, smiled, and then continued, "If you are as good a writer as you have demonstrated with this piece, the summaries will paint some pretty compelling pictures."

"Thanks," said Fran. "I think what you are doing here offers new hope. When I told a couple of my professors, they got excited."

Karen walked back in with the set of questions. "We still have to go over these with Tony, so this is just a beginning, but this gives you an idea of where we want to go."

"We'll preface it with a title and explanation of the whole process," said Fred. "I'm not sure how we can measure it, but it is interesting to speculate about how people from both congregations will be affected by knowing that we will share the summaries with everyone."

"Okay, here they are," said Karen. "You can sort of picture how these will impact both congregations," she added as she passed the sheet to Fran.


1. When people talk about racism, I think it is:

    A. An overworked complaint of liberals

    B. An invisible reality that distorts our society.

    C. A harmful condition affecting all Black citizens.

    D. A challenge that, if understood, could heal our divided society.

2. Being White in this society is:

    A. A normal condition for many of us.

    B. A safe status that has advantages.

    C. An opportunity to misuse power.

    D. An opportunity to be a blessing to others.

3. Bringing up the subject of racism

    A. Makes White people defensive.

    B. Makes Black people angry.

    C. Provides an opportunity for healing conversations.

    D. Doesn't give credit for how far we've come.

4. The biggest barrier to talking about racism is:

    A. The guilt that White people feel.

    B. Black people's belief that nothing will ever change.

    C. Belief that it's all talk, and nothing will ever change.

    D. Religious beliefs that justify racist structures and conditions

5.More Blacks are killed by police than Whites because:

    A. Their behavior deserved it.

    B. It reflects police bias or fear.

    C. Courts often don't hold police accountable.

    D. Blacks don't treat officers with appropriate respect.

6. On average, Black families have one-tenth the wealth of White families because:

    A. Blacks are genetically less business oriented.

    B. Reflects White bias in real estate where you build wealth.

    C. Promotion and advancement favor Whites.

    D. Whites evaluate opportunities based on finances.

7. Being Black in this society:

    A. Means you begin two steps back.

    B. Causes many Whites to be nervous near you.

    C. Is a cause for pride in strength to survive.

    D. Reminds Whites of their racist past.

Fran got getting excited as she read each question. "Can I show these to my professors and the two other classmates working with me?"

Fred looked at Karen, "I think that will be Okay, but make sure they understand the importance of not talking about them with others."

Karen nodded. Then she added, "This may be a little crazy, but wouldn't it be fun to have your co-workers and the two professors try to guess how each congregation will vote ahead of time? You know, what percentage of the Black congregation will pick C for #1, and what percent of the White congregation will pick B? Then, when we share the results with the churches, we could also share what it looks like for a bunch of academics as well."

Fred let out a loud laugh of glee. "This continues to get crazier and crazier -- not crazy bad but crazy good. That is a really creative idea. But we'll spring that as a surprise near the end. I don't want either church to respond thinking about how the academics will see their vote."

"So," continued Fran, "where does this go from here? I mean, after the questions are answered, the summaries are written and shared--then what?"

"We're working on it," said Fred. "Tony and I are trying to figure out how the two congregations can demonstrate how to both be honest about how race affects us and how we might paint a picture for what the world would look like if we could all learn to listen and care about each other."

"I know, I know," said Fran. "Escúcheme! You're trying to teach the whole world how to Escúcheme."

"By gum, I think she's got it," said Karen. "As Fred is fond of saying, you can generate a whole lot more energy and courage if you have a vision of what you are trying to accomplish."

"The vision is good," said Fred, "but we have a whole lot of work to do before we arrive. This is a good beginning, Fran, and I thank that boyfriend that first brought you to the youth group."

"Well," said Fran with a grimace, "this may have been the only good thing to come out of that relationship, but I'm glad it happened if it brought me to this church."

"Ooo, a possible romance gone wrong, I gather."

"Something like that. He really just wasn't my type, but he had good taste in churches, so all was not lost."

"Okay, back to the task," said Fred. "Tony raised the issue of modeling our next step after the Truth and Reconciliation Commission of South Africa. We've both looked at that. We hope that when both congregations have taken the two phases of questions and had them both summarized and interpreted, both congregations will recognize the value of some deep listening to each other." Fred hesitated. "But..." He paused again.

"What is the big 'BUT'?" Karen pushed.

"I think we'll have fun in the first phase," Fred said, "but polite trust is a lot easier to build than intimate trust where you are exposing your vulnerable side."

"Zeke and I were talking about that last night. Our being a mixed marriage and having to be super vigilant about how that affects our children, we're somewhat acquainted with what both congregations are experiencing. I've read up on the Truth and Reconciliation Commission, and those hearings took a lot of courage."

She turned to Fran. "I'm not sure what you know about this, but what they were faced with was years of White oppression and sheer cruelty, and then suddenly the Blacks were in charge. The question was how they were going to bring the two peoples together rather than have a blood bath of revenge."

"As Tony explained it to me," said Fred, "the difference here is that the oppressors (that's us) are still in power, so what is going to convince the Black population, who are still vulnerable in our society, to trust Whites enough to open up? Why would I if I were in their position."

"But you did," said Fran. "You didn't have to go to that store, but you took the risk to stand with Reverend Southgate so that there could be a better solution than either a bloodbath or some other catastrophe."

"Well, thank you. And that helped build some trust --particularly between Tony and me, but how do we do that with large groups of people. Karen, what were you going to share about what you and Zeke were thinking?"

I'm a White, fairly progressive, and justice committed person who is deeply in love with a Black person. I can tell you it is painful to both recognize speak about the privileges I experience in society. I'm not sure how we enable church members to move beyond social friendliness to begin to probe the pain of societal inequality. Blacks have a lot of life experience to cause them to be cautious. Whites have a lot to lose in giving up their society approved privileges.

You do have a way of speaking truth that shatters naivete. How do we help our members grasp a vision of hope that gives them the courage to take some risks for a better world?

What Zeke and I were thinking was what if we began with the leadership of our churches and on a very personal level?"

"Go on."

"You remember that we talked about using either a video presentation or even live streaming? Later we might even experiment with that for some church exchange. For now, as evidence of good faith, what if Zeke and I gave a live example of the TRC? We've talked about this, and he could talk about what it was like growing up Black and a couple of examples of recent experiences. We could also share a little about both our courtship and marriage and what we've experienced. Then I could speak of what it is like to be White and confess what I still benefit from as a White person. Maybe, I'm not sure of this, but maybe I could confess and ask for forgiveness not only from Zeke but also the Mt. Sinai congregation."

Fred gaped at Karen for a few seconds. "I'm not sure how to respond to such a generous offer. However, I want to make sure both you and Zeke understand what you are risking. I know you and Zeke love each other very deeply, but I want to make very sure that we don't put you and your family at risk."

"Fred," Karen looked at him. "I know, and I trust that were the positions reversed, you'd do the same for me. And I know that if I objected like you are, you'd pull yourself up to your full heights and speak in that deep voice you use when you are very serious. You'd say, 'Karen, you are not the person to make this decision. You only have the freedom to accept or deny what is being offered.'"

Fred hesitated and looked a little embarrassed. "You are correct as usual, even if your imitation of my voice is a little off, but you are taking a risk."

"Again, I quote a preacher I once heard when he said, "No act of faith is without risk, but unless you take that risk and trust God for the journey, you can't move forward."

"The danger of preaching," Fred said to Fran, "is that every once in a while, someone will preach your sermon back to you."

Fran grinned. "This is fascinating. I always wondered what was happening behind the scenes in a church. I think you are about to take another step, and I get the honor of witnessing it. Go ahead; I'm listening. Boy, if this works out, my professors are going to be so excited, and my crew might even get our paper published."

"The power of the TRC was helping people move from debating judgment and retribution and turning to the cleansing power of forgiveness and transformation. I want to explore this with Tony, but Karen is opening the window for how we can deepen our trust. If Tony is willing and maybe even another leader in his congregation, after Zeke and Karen have the video of their exchange shown, Tony and I can also make ourselves vulnerable to both congregations as well."

"The hope would be that this might open the possibility of setting up our version of the TRC for our churches. We could structure a series for members of each of our congregations to talk about both the pain and healing that could be possible if we learned to actively listen to each other."

"To reassure you, you set up an appointment with Tony, and then we will arrange a meeting with Zeke as part of it. Fran, I'm counting on you to set up some of your technological magic to film and convey this when we are ready."

"I'll call Tony; meanwhile, Karen, let me be very clear, at any point in this process, you and Zeke can back out. After each of us has done our homework, we'll set up our next appointment. And, THANKS TO BOTH OF YOU."

**FOR CHAPTER RESOURCES AND ADDITIONAL CONTENT, SCAN THIS QR CODE:**
SMcCutchan.Kartra.com/page/CHAPTER22

# CHAPTER 23

# TRUST AND OBEY

Fred was enthusiastic but cautious as he headed towards Tijuana Flats for lunch with Tony. He had heard from Tony that his congregation had enjoyed the first phase of their process. He knew that the incident at the Jimmy's Mini Mart had generated so much positive publicity that the congregations bathed in the positive image of their pastors and felt part of something larger than themselves. Fran's summary of Fourth Presbyterian's first poll also made the papers and received some kind and supportive letters to the editor. It was suddenly positive to be involved in addressing racism, and the naysayers were staying quiet.

His caution, however, was because he knew that when it came crunch time, and it began to touch the individuals, many would revert to being cautious and not wanting to make waves. Still, he couldn't have imagined the many unplanned events that brought them to this stage.

As he opened the restaurant door, he spotted Tony already occupying a booth over in the corner. While they greeted each other with large smiles and a vigorous hug, Fred also knew that Tony was thinking beyond the moment.

When they ordered their meals and began eating, Fred decided it was time to get to work. "Okay, we both got positive vibes from many in our congregations, but you and I know that if we are going to move beyond the feel-good moment, we got some mountains to climb. What's your best guess as to how your people are going to respond to the second survey, which focuses on race and the entrenched system that holds us apart?"

"I think outwardly they will rejoice that our two churches are wanting to work together and maybe build on the positive outcome of our little incident in the Jimmy's Mini Mart, but inwardly, Fred, they'll be afraid. They've been down similar roads before and been disappointed. What about your congregation?"

"They yearn for a better world, but they are still mired in their world. It's one thing to yearn for a better world, where racism is a thing of the past, but it is another thing when it means change, and to get there it is going to cost you."

"Let's review some of the steps we have been talking about," said Tony. "You showed me the second round of questions, and I think they have the possibility of moving us deeper, but eventually, we'll have to move beyond politeness and get into the thick of it."

"I've been thinking about the Truth and Reconciliation Commission idea. I know I was the one who raised the idea, but I can see some big hurdles to get over if we are going to make it work. And the issue of power is a real problem. Remember, in South Africa, the people who confessed to the unjust practices they had been engaged in desperately hoped that the Blacks who were now in power would grant them forgiveness. That's not true here. The Whites are the ones who need to confess, but they also hold power.

If you confess to me about how you've taken advantage of this unjust system and ask me to forgive you, your power is still there. If I refuse to offer forgiveness, you can always say, 'heh, if you don't forgive me, I'm going to wup your ass.'"

To make this really work, we are going to have to get involved in the whole area of reparations. Real forgiveness is not just a verbal statement. It comes with a cost. As we get to know each other better, we'll have to explore how we can demonstrate repair to the broken relationships in our society.

"There is some powerful preparation we are going to have to do with both of our congregations," said Fred.

Tony took a long drink of his coke and said, "You got that right."

"I've had another one of those 'what might not have been moments,' that has morphed into an idea that I want to try out on you."

Tony saw the waitress nearby and waved her over. "Miss, I think this gentleman and I are going to talk about something that might heal the world. In preparation for that, I wonder if you would be so kind as to bring us a plate of nachos and the hottest sauce that you have?"

She glances at Fred and then back at Tony. "Well, if you two are going to heal the world, then the least I can do is get you a plate of nachos. I'll be right back." And she hurried away.

"In a way that I can't explain, it began when we had supper with our wives, and we met Krystal. Because we met her, and because she happened to go into that store where the hostage event was taking place, she chose to call us."

The waitress came back with the nachos. "Have you invented the healing medicine yet?"

"Not quite, but I think we have some of the ingredients. Let me ask you a question."

"OKaaaay," she said with some hesitation.

"I'm not asking about your personal relationships but let me pose a hypothetical situation. Suppose you had had some bad experiences in your last several dating experiences. Then you met another man, and because of your previous experiences, you were somewhat cautious. Then the two of you experienced a difficult situation and this new man not only stuck by you but, at considerable risk to himself, rescued you from the situation. Now my question is, would you be inclined to risk trusting that man and even entertain the possibility that he was a good man?"

"Well, I'm not sure where you are going with this, but given what you've described, I think I'd marry him on the spot."

She smiled and turned away to resume her tasks as a waitress.

"What happened at that store is that you and I took a big risk on behalf of the customers. Because of that, more of both of our congregations are willing to follow us further."

"I think that is true, but I'm not sure where you are going with this."

"My Associate, Karen, happens to be in what is called a 'mixed marriage.' She told me that she and her husband, Zeke, or Ezekiel, talked about it, and they are willing to be videotaped about their own journey. Particularly, they are willing to walk through the Truth and Reconciliation process. Zeke tells his story about both what it is like growing up as a Black boy in this city and their current experience as a mixed-race couple. Then, Karen is willing to walk us through the White confession process illustrating how even someone who considers herself pretty progressive benefits from being White and in need of confession and asking for forgiveness."

"So, you are wondering if we videotaped that and showed it to each of our congregations, it might spark some internal conversations that could help prepare for some of our people doing the same. I like it."

"I'm also wondering if we could take it one step further. I'm wondering if you and I could walk through our shared experience, both with your son and with the store incident?" ventured Fred.

"Do you think that would advance the possibility of this process taking on some legs?"

"The questions and sharing we have in the first two phases of our project will have warmed them up to the subject of race and some of the challenges it presents to how we should live as a church and society," said Tony.

"Yet, both of us know," said Fred, "that that is just skimming the surface. If we do a good job with the video of Karen and Zeke, we will have personalized the issue for both of our people."

"And what will we gain from sharing your story and mine?" asked Tony.

"My hope is two things will happen. First, your personal story about what happened to Eric and both the facts and emotions you and Ariel went through could provide my congregation with a glimpse at the personal impact racism has in our society. By the way, how is his recovery going?"

"Actually, remarkably well. The bullets pierced his body, but they didn't sever his spine. I'd say in another couple of months, with good physical therapy, he'll slowly begin to walk again." Tony scowled and quietly cursed, "Damn-it, Fred, we still have to go to court and use lawyers to prove that a scared boy with a Hershey in one hand and a dark paper-wrapped Subway in the other wasn't threatening an inexperienced officer with a gun."

Fred sighed. "Here is an example of what most of my White congregation doesn't understand. Hell, I didn't even understand that this is the type of threat a Black family must worry about on a daily basis. But that is even more reason why what we are doing is important."

"I'm sorry to be cynical, Fred, but don't get your hopes up that things are going to change. We've been down this road before."

"That's a good caution but sitting back in our comfortable pews isn't going to help either. And if you are willing to share your story, and I share how this experience and the store experience has forced me to grow spiritually, maybe, because it is personal, it will help our congregation realize that this is the reality in which the Gospel is lived. We're not just making this up. We live in two different worlds, and the Gospel hopes that we might become one people."

"Well, I guess part of what it means to live the Gospel is to swim against the tide. Despite quite a bit of evidence that can make you wonder, I still cling to the hope that God is still out there inviting us to a different way of life; but damn, I continue to struggle with that forgiveness part."

"Tony, I've not even begun to face the same reality as you and Ariel and Eric. I cling to the hope that our faith is real too. That story in Luke where Jesus is hanging on the cross and asks God to forgive the people because they don't know what they are doing haunts me."

"That's where the rubber hits the road, isn't it?" said Tony. "Do you recall that story that Desmond Tutu told of the soldier when asked after the war whether he forgave the enemy who had held him captive? When he responded that he would never forgive them, his friend responded, 'then I guess they still hold you in prison, don't they?' The reason I struggle so hard with this is that I know that until I can get rid of my anger and, yes, even hate at what the police did to my son, I will never be free to be the person that God calls me to be."

"The power of Tutu's work with forgiveness for me," said Fred, "is that it wasn't just an intellectual exercise. He and Mandela, as well as many others, had every justifiable reason to hate those who had tortured and killed so many of their neighbors. When he talks of forgiveness, it challenges all the logic of our world."

"Do you remember when those Amish families offered forgiveness to those killers who had shot their children in that school? The general society was shocked, but it was just like God hearing Jesus' prayer to forgive those who crucified him."

"So that is where the video comes in," said Tony. "After we've shown our people the video of us being willing to be vulnerable enough to share our stories, that might be an encouragement for members of both of our congregations to share some of their stories."

"Heh, this is beginning to tie together," said Fred. "Each of us has our personal stories, many of which are filled with personal pain that has shaped our lives. And in this messed up world, like the soldier in Tutu's story, each of us is locked into our own personal prisons."

"According to Tutu, the only way we can get free is if I can listen deeply to your story and you can listen deeply to mine, and then there is at least a chance that we can write a new story together that overcomes the divisions that threaten us."

"And the videos at least give a glimpse of how that might work in the lives of very human people that our people know and like."

Tony stood up. "Let me refill your drink before I add one more complex possibility on you."

"What have you got in mind?"

"Just sit there and speculate while I get you some more sugar water. This forgiveness thing is beginning to take on new dimensions for me." He smiled and walked towards the soda fountain, leaving Fred to speculate.

When he returned, he set the drinks down and took his seat. "I can't believe I'm even saying this, but I think faith is advanced when you live as if it is true rather than just talk about it."

"Okay," Fred said hesitantly. What crazy idea have you got in mind?"

"You've added Zeke and Karen to this new story that we are writing. What do you think might be the result if we could figure out a way to add Tyler, our hostage-taker, to the mix, and maybe even those police officers who are probably still living because you intervened before I attacked them?"

"I'd say that we would be exploring forgiveness at ground level. Of course, our people may not want anything to do with it, but it's sure worth exploring. Frankly, so many unexpected things have happened in these last few days that I am game for anything."

"Let's start with visiting Tyler at the prison. I think he is a living testimony to how deep listening can have a transforming effect. I must admit that that was the first experience I've had with being hugged by a man holding a sawed-off shotgun in one hand and a Glock 19 in the other."

"Who knew that ministry could be so much fun?" laughed Fred as they got up to leave.

 **FOR CHAPTER RESOURCES AND ADDITIONAL CONTENT, SCAN THIS QR CODE:**

SMcCutchan.Kartra.com/page/CHAPTER23

# CHAPTER 24

# A MODEL OF FORGIVENESS

Fred and Tony entered the prison and approached the lobby of the visitation room where they could talk to an inmate. The walls of the registration room were a dull gray. There were no windows or pictures on the wall. A series of wooden benches provided places to sit while they waited to enter the visitation rooms.

Fred glanced around. "You know it wouldn't cost much to brighten this room, get some comfortable chairs for the families while they wait, and maybe even play some pleasant music. The people who come here are not prisoners; they are just the families who are trying to offer support."

"I'm not trying to sound pompous, but 'Welcome to my world.'"

"You have members in here?

"It's part of our Black world," Tony said. "They did a study in 2017 and though Black people are twelve percent of the population, Black prisoners constitute thirty-three percent of the prison population. A Black boy born in 2001 has a one in three chance of going to prison while a White boy has a one in seventeen chance. I've visited quite a few people here."

"I've been here to visit a few people, but I'm not sure there are any of my church families in here. Either that or they are too ashamed to admit it."

"We can't afford to be ashamed. This recent effort to discover who is in prison but really innocent found that 47% of those found to be falsely convicted are Black men. Those men have to have their dignity restored so they can get a new life. The church is one of the first places that can offer such healing."

They approached the officer behind the plastic window where they signed in.

"Reverend Southgate, it's nice to see you again. Who are you here to see?"

Once Tony had identified Tyler Fishermen, the officer handed them both some papers to fill out. "While you are doing that, I'll call back there and get a room ready, and Tyler brought up."

Soon they walked through the doors that opened onto another gray hallway and led to a small room. When they entered, there was a small table and chairs in the otherwise bare room. Within minutes, the other door in the room opened, and Tyler was ushered in. He was seated at the table across from Fred and Tony. He bowed his head and was silent.

"Mr. Fishermen," Tony said, "I told you previously that if you allowed us to have a peaceful resolution to that incident at the Jimmy's Mini Mart, we would help make sure that your side of the story was told. Part of that belongs in the court, but we think we may have a way to share it with the larger public."

"Why you doing that? I almost killed both of you and a lot of other people. You don't owe me nothing."

"Can I call you Tyler?"

He nodded his head.

"Tyler, what you did in that store wasn't right, and I won't pretend to you that it was. But those stories you told about your experience at work and how some people treated your wife aren't right either. And I suspect that there were a lot of other times in your life that you and your family were disrespected."

Tyler straightened up and looked at both of them. "I know I did wrong, but I just couldn't take it no more."

"Even if you still had to do your time, if you had a chance to tell some of those stories to say a couple of hundred people who would at least listen to you, would you want to do that?" asked Fred.

"Why would they want to listen to me?"

"It wouldn't be anything official. Members of both our churches want to understand how racism is tearing our society apart. You're telling your story might help other people feel like they are not alone with their experiences."

"Could my wife and child be there to listen? It might make them feel like I was doing some good."

"We would have to do it by filming you telling your story, but if you do that, I'll guarantee you that they will get to both see you tell it and also see that other people, both Black and White, are hearing it."

Tyler sat even straighter and grinned a little. "If Johnny saw me like that, he'd probably think I was in the movies. He'd like that. And maybe it would help my wife not feel so ashamed to have other people hear how wrong those idiots were who treated her that way.

Yeah, I'll do that if you show me how."

Before their visit, Tony had talked to the prison warden, and she had agreed to permit the filming in the visitation room. For the rest of their visit, Fred and Tony spoke with Tyler about what he would say and how they would film it.

When the guard returned to get Tyler, they all rose and Tyler said, "I don't deserve this, and I will accept my punishment, but I want you to know how grateful I am that you are doing this. Do you know how good it feels to think I can do something that my boy and wife will be proud of?"

"Heh, Lewis," he said to the guard, "I'm going to be in the movies. Maybe if I tell them how good you are at being a guard, they'll give you a raise. Wouldn't that be a kick in the pants?"

They all laughed as Lewis escorted Tyler back to his cell.

As they left the building, Fred put his hand on Tony's shoulder. "Didn't Jesus say something about coming to set the prisoners free? Tyler may not be physically free, but I think we just played a role in setting his spirit free."

Tony laughed. "There are lots of frustrations in the ministry, and there have been several times when I just wanted to walk away from it all, but it's moments like these that make it seem all worthwhile."

"Okay, you talk to the warden about all the rules we have to follow," said Fred, "and I will call a cameraman and see if we can set it up for two days from now. I'm going to call that reporter who was so nice in the interview. I can promise that if he will provide a good cameraman and keep it under wraps until we give the release, we can offer him an exclusive that should make some good footage on the evening news."

Tony turned towards Fred. "Nothing will ever justify the shooting of my son, but if we can pull this off, we might help our people experience a real blessing and at least demonstrate publicly how God can transform evil into good. Thanks, Fred, I think I've just experienced one of those thin moments you are always talking about."

"This is getting interesting," said Fred. "Why don't you sketch out a basic framework for how we would pull off our initial TRC meeting while I think through the questions we might use for both of our congregations for the next interview phase?"

They hugged and parted to think through what needed to happen in the next phase of this adventure.

 **FOR CHAPTER RESOURCES AND ADDITIONAL CONTENT, SCAN THIS QR CODE:**

SMcCutchan.Kartra.com/page/CHAPTER24

# CHAPTER 25

# MY STORY, YOUR STORY

Ariel met Tony at one of their favorite restaurants. She was sitting at a table watching for him out the window. When she saw him pop out of his car with a bounce in his steps, she let out a long breath and felt her shoulders relax. She knew that Tony both looked forward to and was anxious about the visit to the prison. It wasn't the prison. He regularly visited church family members there and had a good relationship with many of the personnel. This time, however, he was not just providing pastoral comfort to an inmate. This time he was going with his new friend, Fred, and talking to a prisoner who had almost killed them. More importantly, they were going to ask that prisoner to help them put a dent in the racist structure of our society that is over 400 years old. How is that not a set up for failure? And yet Tony was experiencing a growing optimism that there might be some hope in the world. Even though she had had a life of trying to trust that there could be a better world, the numerous disappointments she had experienced made her extremely cautious about exposing herself to hope.

She looked up with a smile as he came through the door and was greeted with a smile in return. She rose to greet him. As she moved into his arms for a hug, she said, "You look like you have had a very good morning."

"I know it's risky, but I'm almost daring to believe that Fred is genuine, and that God might be working through us for a better world."

"Praise the Lord and pass the appetizers. Tell me all about it."

"First of all, the visit went about as good as you could want. The gunman, Tyler, is an excellent example of what this world can do to beat an essentially good man down. And Fred brought up the idea of doing a video interview with him and showing it to both of our congregations. Tyler will talk about the pressures that led up to the event and the power of our intervening and listening to him. It should be a dramatic illustration of just what we are suggesting.

After a pause, Tony turned serious and said, "There is one little item that I need to talk to you about, however."

"I was beginning to get happy until that last sentence. What are you planning--a jailbreak?"

"No, Fred and I think it might help prepare both of our congregations for their dialogue on racism if we told our story as well."

"Told our story? Exactly how much of our story are you talking about? Do we want to talk about how a man planning on going into the ministry got a little carried away one night and almost raped me in his jeep rambler?"

Tony grinned. "That was justifiable passion given that outfit you had on."

"The only way I could get the man's head out of the theological cloud and move towards marrying me."

"Well, it worked, thanks be to God, but I didn't exactly have that little incident in mind."

"OK, tell me more, and I'll keep that image in mind while I consider your offer."

"You know that his associate, Karen, and her husband who is Black, are going to share on a video some of their experiences of race. Fred has asked if we, as two pastoral couples, would be willing to share our experiences of the impact of racism on our lives -- especially around the shooting of our son."

As he said it, he saw Ariel wince at the memory, but she quickly recovered. "If Lilly is willing to try that, then so am I. I want to talk to Lilly ahead of time. There is a lot of that experience that I still would like to process."

"That's fantastic. We'd cover the waterfront with the video of an inter-racial couple, two pastors and their spouses, and a Black laborer and his wife who is often invisible in our society."

"I can see that that could be impactful, but where is it leading? I've always heard you be disdainful of lots of pretty words but no action."

The waitress brought them their lunch. Tony said a brief prayer, including thanks for what had been happening today and for his wife and her support. "Let's enjoy this wonderful meal as I explain what I'm beginning to see as a positive possibility."

As they ate, Tony began to explain. "You have heard me talk about Desmond Tutu and the Truth and Reconciliation Commission? I hope that we can discover a way to make use of that example for the church."

"But you have been skeptical that our people would be willing to have enough trust to genuinely tell their story with a White audience present because, unlike South Africa, Whites still hold power to hurt us if what we said upset them."

"Very true, and I'm still hesitant about that, but consider this. What if Tyler told his story first about how our racial society drove him to violence. It's a story that most of our people will both understand and be grateful that, so far, they have escaped exploding that way themselves -- even though they probably have come close to it numerous times. And as they watch that story, they will also see how the Gospel can help transform evil into good."

"Next, if you are willing, we'll tell our story, which addresses the fear of most parents in our congregation. We might even share a little about events that led up to it. But then the story begins to morph into a story that holds some promise of hope that the world can be better."

"And then Fred and Lilly will tell their story and how the violence of racism has impacted their lives," said Ariel.

"They'll tell their story of some of the racism in our society that they now understand and their part in it. But they will also tell the story of how, when they couldn't escape it, that night at the hospital, they turned and joined with us. Here will be two couples, Black and White, beginning to write a new story that allows God to begin to give birth to hope."

"So, their story, our story, and Tyler's story, all of which could have ended in tragedy, shows how you can begin to write a new story."

"Even though we must face it in a way that makes us vulnerable, we can write a better story together. I guess that is a little like Jesus and the disciples who had to become vulnerable before they experienced the resurrection."

Tony had a big fork full of food headed towards his mouth. Suddenly he stopped and laid the fork down and stared at Ariel. "How was I so blessed to meet and marry you."

"Nice of you to decide that marriage was better than rape. Though I certainly would have been tempted that night," she grinned.

"We'll come back to that subject later tonight," he smiled and suggestively raised his right eyebrow. "For now, I think you know what we are trying to work out for our two congregations. We hope that by our being willing to be vulnerable with them in sharing our stories and seeing how that resulted in us being able to work together to write a new, more creative, more blessed story together, maybe they will be willing to trust us enough to share in that process between our two congregations."

"That's exciting if a little scary. How would you set it up?"

"We've still got a lot of details to work out, but we'd have a different set of questions than the first time. This time the central focus would be on race, racism, Whites and Blacks. Since they will know ahead of time that both congregations will see the results' graph, I suspect that they will be a little more cautious. However, it will still show the different perspectives even within each congregation and certainly between the congregations.

"Then," Tony continued, "we will announce the date for the video presentation. We can stream it to church each of our church's websites so that people can see it in the privacy of their own homes. We'll also have a public showing. We have been debating whether that should be in one big gathering of the two congregations or at each of our separate congregations."

"It will probably be pretty emotional. I can see an advantage to both ways," said Ariel.

"We would want to follow it up with an explanation of our version of the Truth and Reconciliation process. They wouldn't need to commit that evening, but our goal is to create a safe atmosphere in which Black members who are willing can tell their stories of how race has impacted their lives and families. We'd structure it so they could talk about both the general impact from childhood and some specific, more recent experiences.

"We'd explain how the naming of the hurts and knowing it has been heard can liberate them to move beyond living a wounded life and discovering the True Self that God desires in each of them. If they are willing, we'll have them do that live, but another alternative will be to have them be videotaped, or if necessary, write it out and have someone else read it."

"I can see the value of your initial videos giving them courage. It's scary to be that vulnerable. But what about the White people? That could get pretty heavy hearing all of that?"

"This is where it gets pretty tricky, but here is what we hope. In addition to Karen, Fred, and Ellen telling their story, Fred thinks he can at least find several White members who might also speak, especially if they've seen the video and had a chance to think about it."

Tony continued, "What we would ask them to do is to talk about their growing awareness of systemic racism and their part in it and to turn in the face of the stories they've heard and genuinely ask for forgiveness. That's not going to be easy. Not all Black people will want to offer forgiveness, but we can make a beginning."

"Because of all the recent publicity around you two, you should get a pretty good response from both congregations."

"I think both Fred and I should come into that meeting with a commitment to establish at least one, maybe two or three task forces, to begin to work on ways we can put flesh on our new story. When Fred and I were at the prison, he was so struck by the prison's drabness that he started talking about painting, getting new chairs, and maybe some music. It's that type of practical thing that could move us forward."

"Oh, by the way, your Presbytery Exec called. It seems he's read some of those articles in the newspaper and wants to be brought up to date," said Ariel. "You may be starting something bigger than you realize."

"He has often seemed most interested in keeping the peace, but given the events of the last several weeks, I'm beginning to believe in miracles. I'll call him back tomorrow. I've got a few things to do at the office, and I have an important date with my wife that I don't want to miss."

The waitress brought the bill and credit card receipt. Tony began to fill it out.

"Tony, I think this is the beginning of something special. To celebrate it, why don't you leave an extra-generous tip?"

He nodded, completed the receipt, and helped Ariel get up from the table.

 **FOR CHAPTER RESOURCES AND ADDITIONAL CONTENT, SCAN THIS QR CODE:**
SMcCutchan.Kartra.com/page/CHAPTER25

# CHAPTER 26

# SETTING UP THE CONVERSATION

"If we are going to reach beyond the activist faithful and include a large part of each of our congregations in this conversation, we need to attract even the reluctant members to participate," said Tony. "There will be some of my people who feel they have been beaten up enough and don't want to make themselves vulnerable one more time.

And from what you have said, some of your people are afraid that such a conversation will just end up accusing them of being racist. Both groups lack a vision of hope that makes the effort worthwhile."

"Our idea is to provide them a little safer venue to introduce the idea and reinforce a vision of hope as we move towards our version of the Truth and Reconciliation Commission," added Fred. "And I think our video may be a safe place to both explain what we are doing and to provide some sample conversations."

A week later, Tony and Fred met to review the video that they had created. They hoped that the video would introduce both of their congregations to the larger process of a bi-congregational conversation.

Their idea was to begin by explaining to all who viewed the video the purpose and the promise of such a conversation. They watched the video begin with some background information on Desmond

Tutu and how the Truth and Reconciliation Commission's works.

The video began, "We, Fred, pastor of Fourth Presbyterian, and I, Tony, Pastor of Mt. Sinai, have been seeking God's guidance about how to apply the lessons from Desmond Tutu and the Truth and Reconciliation Commission to our churches. This video is our introduction to a process by which our members can tell their stories of how racism has affected their lives and how we seek as a faith community to rewrite the story."

"Our hope is that by seeing this video," said Fred, "you will see examples of your neighbors telling their stories and be encouraged to tell your story at least to yourself or a good friend. By doing so, you might take the first step beyond the racist plague that is hurting our society. We want this to be the first step towards our churches showing our society a better way."

With that opening, the video continued by explaining the process that they were proposing.

THE FRAMEWORK FOR THE MEETINGS

The TRC for churches follows a four-fold framework.

1.    People who have been hurt in human interaction can move from victimhood to healed purpose and meaning in life through being able to tell their story.

2.    The process permits them to name the hurts they have experienced. Having given voice to their pains and knowing it has been heard opens them to the possibility of being liberated to discover their true self as God intends.

3.    This also offers the offending population the opportunity

to seek forgiveness for the unfair society's structure of which they have been a part.

4.  If such confession is both voiced and forgiveness is given, then there is the possibility of renewed connection where there had been division. A witness to a richer world that draws upon all the gifts God has offered is advanced.

Our idea is that your pastors and the leaders of your congregations will arrange for a community conversation.

They will provide a comfortable and safe setting to interview and listen to those who wish to tell their story. Where appropriate, they will provide a person from the team to accompany the speaker and offer support.

"Shouldn't we offer a printout of this next section that people can take with them and reflect on. It's always good to have a printout."

"I agree," said Fred. "Maybe all we have to do is have a transcript of what we said on the video."

The video continued. "An individual who wishes to speak will be placed on a schedule and permitted to speak without interruption for an agreed-upon period of time. While the leadership may pose questions for clarification, no challenges or judgments are acceptable.

There is a two-fold perspective for the conversations and an umbrella purpose. The umbrella purpose is to submit to the hope that there is a God-given potential to advance the reconciliation and enrichment of humanity with confession and forgiveness.

Here is how we see it happening.

1.  Black participants are invited to share the examples of their

experiences with racism in their life. They could include both what it was like growing up in our society and/or any specific incidents that they desire to describe in their current life. We encourage storytellers to share both the factual description and the emotional impact. We'll give you an example of how this would happen.

2. White participants should speak on a more confessional level. They are asked to both describe their level of awareness of White privilege and the impact it has had on them as they increasingly recognize how it impacts their Black neighbors. This includes not only systemic benefits but also the multiple microaggressions that we not only commit but also observe without raising objections.

That will not be easy, but again we will provide you an example from a member of Fourth church.

While the pain of injustice is real, the church's faith invites us to move from getting revenge for our hurt to being open to a restoration of a relationship that could have been. We move from:

Retributive justice (making them pay) to

Restorative justice (healing the brokenness of community).

We invite our White members to move from denial to acceptance of our part in the imbalance of community. While none of us owned slaves directly, nor do we deliberately conspire to discriminate or treat unjustly people who are different from us, we benefit from a variety of conditions in our history and our present context.

A significant factor in this imbalance is the distribution of power within the community. While it can apply to anyone, let us speak specifically to Blacks and Whites in our society. There are more

Whites than Blacks who hold positions that can shape the justice system, economic investments, the condition of our schools, and most of the other institutions that can provide or deny opportunity in people's lives.

Be honest with yourselves. If there were two people, Black and White, and you both had the same quality of parents, education, and talent, which of you would most likely prosper most in thirty years of working. While there are always exceptions, on the whole, which would you wager might come out ahead.

Even if you as an individual want to be equal, the system itself gives unfair advantages to one group over the other.

That is how we envision it, but here is the structure of how we envision it at a two-congregation meeting. Again, we will explain it on this video and provide you with a handout that explains how this meeting will take place.

We will convene a meeting of the two congregations at a banquet hall where we can sit around tables and talk with each other.

1. You pastors will convene the meeting with a prayer to God to both hear our pain and our stories and bless us with restorative options.

2. Several Black volunteers will share their stories about their life experiences, including facts and emotions. The reports are received without judgment or question except for clarification.

3. Several White volunteers will confess to their awareness of the benefits they have received from being White and any sense of responsibility they recognize for not challenging racist conditions,

advocating for change in their community, or seeking greater healing in their immediate lives or their larger community.

Fred and I will demonstrate as we do in this video, by sharing our own stories.

"Fred and I will briefly share our stories of what brought us to this place. We will be brief because you already know some of the major events. For you at Fourth Presbyterian, you know me as Fred's colleague in ministry and his friend. We've always treated each other as equals and supported each other as we tried to interpret the Gospel as it applies to the various issues in our society."

"The events that led up to where we are now began," said Fred, "as we were riding together coming home from a Presbytery meeting. We stopped for a quick bite and just to have a friendly conversation. During our conversation, Tony mentioned his concern; no, I'd say it was fear, though I didn't understand that at the time. He spoke about his son, Eric, approaching when he'd be getting his driver's license. It was the first real in-depth conversation we had ever had about the difference between being a White parent and a Black parent."

"That led to a brief conversation about racial differences and a promise to talk more later," said Tony. "I will confess that though I liked Fred, I didn't expect it to go anywhere. You folks at Mt. Sinai have tiptoed into such conversation with White colleagues and soon realized that you had better back off."

"Then our two worlds came crashing into each other," Fred said as he put a hand on Tony's shoulder. "You from Mt. Sinai will remember with horror the night Eric was shot by the police and clinging to his life at the city's Hospital. Ariel called me and asked me to take her to the hospital, where Tony was already stalking the halls waiting to see what would happen."

"From that night on, Fred has crossed the invisible boundaries that often keep us slightly apart. Many of you at Fourth have experienced his commitment to confronting racism, both the personal and institutional variety. I would say to you folks that I understand why some of his actions have upset and even angered either you or some of your neighbors in your church."

Tony continued, "You may be aware, but many Blacks have survived in this society by being conflict avoiders. Some in my church were rather upset at some of my anti-racist sermons and programs."

"But that all changed that day at the Jimmy's Mini Mart store. As you will see in a minute, what started as an armed robbery soon became a turning point for both of our churches," said Fred.

"I think," said Tony, "it is best to begin by letting Tyler tell his own story. Ladies and gentlemen, may I introduce Tyler Fishermen, who Fred and I met at Jimmy's Mini Mart."

Then the camera switched to Tyler dressed in his orange prison outfit. "UH ..., My name is Tyler Fishermen; my wife is Jasmine, and we have a son, Barney. He's ten. The pastors asked me to tell you my story. My dad didn't finish high school." Tyler laughed nervously. "He got tossed out when he was a junior for taking on three honkies -- oh, sorry, for fighting three White guys who were messing with him. He had to get a job to help support his mom, and when he got married, he worked two jobs -- digging ditches and helping in a construction project. He worked hard, but he drank hard too. He died when I was 15 of a heart attack.

"I had an uncle who loved to work on old cars. He got an old wreck from a junkyard and taught me a lot about machines. When I was 18, my uncle was arrested for possession of drugs. They came down hard on him, and he got 15 years for possession and dealing. I think they just made the dealing bit up, but he didn't have any fancy lawyer to help him. Before he went to prison, he gave me the old junker we were working on, and I got it working smooth.

"I met Jasmine, who was working part-time at the drive-in of a local Dairy Queen near where I worked. We liked each other from the start. She was really fine. I got into a couple of fights because some guys decided they could paw her. She didn't deserve that type of treatment.

"She got pregnant the second year we were dating, and I dropped out of school to get a job to support her and our new baby. Since I was good at machines, I got a job at a factory that used a lot of machines. The problem was that White guys ran the factory, and most workers were also White. People would call the other colored workers and me all sorts of names. When we got upset, since there were more of them than us, they would just laugh about it like they were so cool. The foreman was also White, and he just let it slide.

"Since I was good at machines, I often saw things that could be repaired or run better. When I tried to explain that to my White supervisor, he would get angry. We often got into arguments. He even used the N-word once, and I got fed up with alwaconstantlyng insulted. I stood up and told him he shouldn't talk that way. He just looked at me real hard and told me not to let the door slam on my way out.

"I hadn't taken the car to work that day because I was low on gas, so I just started walking towards home. I was furious, feeling like it wasn't fair. When I walked by Jimmy's Mini Mart, I remembered all the times when Jasmine came home in tears because some guy tried to feel her up or make some nasty comments. Suddenly it felt like the whole world was continually picking on us, and it was just unfair.

"I know I shouldn't have done it, but I lost it and thought someone should pay. I had a Glock 19 in my lunch box, and I just went in and started shouting and threatening everyone. I know it was crazy thinking, but somehow, I thought if a few people died -- including the store manager who was one of those who insulted my wife -- then maybe someone would pay attention.

"Well, you know the story from there. Someone had called these two preachers, and they started talking to me. No, more than that, they started listening to me. They not only heard what I said but also seemed to hear how I felt. It cleared my mind, but I thought I was in too deep, and there was no way out.

"Then it was not only them but some of the people in the store, ones I was holding a gun on and threatening to shoot. They began to listen and understand what I was going through. I couldn't hurt them now, so I let them arrest me. I deserve to be punished, but the pastors here thought it might do some good for you to hear my story. And since this is being filmed, the pastors said my boy would see this, too. Hi, Barney, be good to your mother. She is the best. Maybe even my wife can forgive me for the way I messed up."

Tony came back on camera. "You later heard the story of how Fred and I were able to diffuse the moment by listening to him and the hurt he experienced in his life. Like all of us, he is an imperfect individual, but we believe God can use him just like God used many imperfect people in the Bible for a greater purpose."

The story of racism doesn't just apply to people who are barely scraping out a living. For example, we want you to hear the story of two professionals.

Hear the story of Fred's Associate Pastor and her husband. May I present to you Ezekiel and Karen Derringer?"

The screen transitioned to a tall Black man dressed in a conservative blue suit and a woman dressed in clerical garb who stood by his side.

"My name is Ezekiel Derringer, and this is my wife, Karen. She is an Associate Pastor at Fourth Presbyterian. As you can see, I'm Black, and she is White. We were asked to share what it's like to be in a mixed marriage in this society. I guess the fact that we even have to talk about it suggests that, as a society, we have never learned to respond comfortably to the issue of race.

"They asked me to begin by sharing how I experienced racism as I was growing up, and then Karen will do the same. Then we will talk about our experience as a married couple with two children,

Gary (age 12) and Patty (age 8).

"First, both of my parents are professionals. My father is a professor at a nearby college, and my mother has been a bank vice president. I first became aware of the impact of race when my parents were called into my school. I had tested to be eligible for the advanced class, and the counselor wasn't sure if I would be overwhelmed by the advanced level and wanted to explain her logic to my parents. My parents were furious at this, but I learned from the experience that my skin color had influenced the school's reasoning.

"It was the beginning of a long and tiring journey of people underestimating my ability based on my skin color. I was particularly good with numbers and became an accountant, but almost every promotion I got as I progressed in my profession had one of two messages. Either I was told that I was the first African American to achieve that position, or it was assumed that I received the promotion because Affirmative Action gave me an advantage. After four hundred years, you wouldn't think I would be the first one in any position.

My parents had " The Talk" with me as I approached the age to get my license. Unlike many of my White friends, I was never told that the police were a resource I could trust and turn to in a moment of need. Instead, I was told I would probably be stopped by the police even when I had done nothing wrong. That has happened several times, including recently. My parents told me to be overly cautious when that happened. I was to keep my hands where they could be seen, don't make any sudden moves, and always explain politely what I was doing when I reached for my license, a package in the car, or even releasing my seat belt and exiting the vehicle.

"I was also taught by my parents how to observe any new situation and prepare for the unexpected. They were right, but it meant I could rarely just relax and enjoy any new experience. I never went to a party, an interview, a sports event, or even a strange building where I didn't check for potential threats among those present. I can instantly sense the rise in tension when I join a virtually all-White group."

Karen spoke up. "Let me comment on that. I was raised by two progressive parents who taught me to treat others with respect. I was in the Peace Corps before I went to seminary, and I would have told you that I was not prejudiced and abhorred racism in society. When I arrived at seminary, I met Ezekiel because he worked in the seminary business office, where I paid my bills. When we started dating, my racial education took a major leap forward. When I was in the Peace Corps, I knew I was an outsider, and I had to act accordingly. What I didn't understand was that, to a large degree, most African Americans have to live that way in this country always being alert to the often-unspoken rules of each group with which you interact. I often walk around, assuming I'm normal. Zeke has to assume he is not normal until circumstances tell him otherwise."

Zeke spoke again. "Being alert to all the signals around you can be exhausting. There were several times when we were dating that Karen didn't understand why I was hesitant to attend a social event, engage in a debate, try to secure a loan, or challenge a myth about the Black community. I was frequently asked to explain why certain racial groups behaved this way or that. Being a mixed couple seemed to raise the ante. Karen was approached several times about what it was like to be with a Black man. There is a myth that we Black men might be more exciting for White women."

"If you value your life, you'll never try to share and compare," Karen said as she punched him on the arm.

"Heh, I'm not that crazy."

"I do want to return to one subject as a reasonably liberal White woman. I didn't realize how many assumptions I made. The easiest way to explain it was that I just assumed since I wasn't overtly prejudiced, I wasn't part of our culture's racist side. Living with Zeke and raising two children that reflect our mixed races has shown me several circumstances where I had an advantage just because I am White. No one looks at me with suspicion when I shop in stores. It's easier to get a loan. If my application is accepted or I get a reward, no one questions if that is an example of reverse racism. When I walked around in society before I met Ezekiel, I didn't even think about my race. I thought I was just normal. Even good-hearted and intellectually competent people have been shaped by both personal myths and culturally unfair structures. Now I must prepare our children to live in that situation without being scarred in their development. "

Fred came back into the video. "Now we are going to take a shift in this video. Our plan and our invitation to you, the members of our two churches, is for as many of us as possible to take part in both telling our stories and listening to the stories of each other. We are following an adaption of a plan followed by Bishop Desmond Tutu from South Africa. When the country was about ready to blow apart, they devised what was called the Truth and Reconciliation Commission.

"It is based on Tutu's belief that there can be no true reconciliation or hope for the future without forgiveness. Forgiveness, Tutu believed, requires us to be willing to tell our personal stories, with all their hopes and pains, and be ready to ask for and receive the forgiveness of those who have been hurt. If that happens, and there is no guarantee that it will, there is the possibility that those who have faced their guilt and responsibility can together write a new story of hope and joy.

"We'll go over the details of that later. Still, first, we want to provide you the possibility to truly hear the stories of Blacks and Whites in this racist society and consider the possibility of rewriting our stories together as Christian brothers and sisters.

"We hope that by seeing some ordinary but very brave members of both of our churches tell their stories, you will grow more comfortable with offering your stories as well. Remember that the people you are about to hear are neither good nor bad people but members who seek to live the faith like you and I do. "

"With that in mind, allow me to introduce to you Barrie Cranford, a member of Fourth Presbyterian church."

A strongly built White man in his fifties moved into the camera. He was dressed in black slacks with a red sweater over a dress shirt. While he looked a little nervous, it was clear that he had experience in speaking to a crowd.

He began by thanking Tony and Fred for inviting him to speak. Then he turned to the camera. "I also want to thank the members of Mt. Sinai as well as my fellow members from Fourth for arranging this conversation. I am growing to believe that this is a meaningful conversation and may well contribute to both of our churches' spiritual maturity.

"I must admit until this conversation came up, like Karen said, I didn't even think about my skin color. I assumed that I achieved whatever I did or made progress because of my efforts and skills. I think it would irritate me to be constantly thinking about how the color of my skin affected my ability to be a success or to hear the suggestion that the color of my skin affected my promotion, either up or down. I guess that's why many of us get upset when it is suggested that there is such a thing as White privilege as if we had been given a special break.

"I try to be fair and treat others with respect. When this was first raised for me, my first reaction was 'I don't apologize for being White,' and I don't appreciate being lumped in with those numb skulls who are always marching around waving the Confederate flag and shouting about protecting the country from colored people who don't know their place. When people talked about White privilege, I thought they were nuts. I believed in the Constitution that said we are all created equal, and while there are a few laws that need to be changed because they are unfair, mostly our society provides the freedom to achieve whatever you want if you are willing to work hard for it.

"I'm beginning to realize there are many unintentional ways that I embarrass or even insult some of my friends of color. More than once, I've asked a Black friend to speak for all Black people. Being a parent in this crazy age is scary enough, but it didn't even occur to me to caution my children about the police or tell them they will have to be twice as smart to come out equal with the majority of their classmates. Good grief, we are the majority. We don't have to be twice as good to get in with the good group. When I was in a social group and saw a bunch of Blacks wanting to eat together, I thought to myself, 'why don't they mix with the rest of us?' It only recently occurred to me that we Whites are a group ourselves. We also need to mix with the rest of the party. "

Tony re-entered the frame and, having thanked Barrie Cranford for his presentation, turned to face the camera. "Now, I am going to introduce to you a member of my church, Mt. Sinai. She is a very strong woman who has faced many challenges in life, some racial and many just parts of our everyday living. She has always done it with her chin up high and dignity on her face. She has quite a story to tell.

"Ladies and gentlemen, I present to you, Mrs. Latisha Smith.

A short, dark, heavy-set woman came on to the screen.

"My name is Latisha Smith. I'm a single mom trying to raise three children. To do that, I have to hold two jobs. I'm a cleaning lady at the Bright Villa Hotel, and on the weekends and some evenings, I'm a waitress at a restaurant. I'm blessed to have a good mother who helps me out with my children's care, and they help out a lot. Like all children, they occasionally get into trouble, but sometimes I think they are treated too harshly and not given the benefit of the doubt just because they are Black and maybe because their mother doesn't always dress up real fancy when she goes out.

"Mostly I just try to do my job and not think about race too much, but I must admit it gets tiring. I try to ignore racial slurs and respond pleasantly when someone calls me 'girl' or 'heh missy' when they want something extra at the hotel. After ten years of doing a good job and applying several times for openings as a supervisor, it is frustrating to repeatedly see them hire a young supervisor who acts as if she is the only one who has ever made a bed before. It's hard when you know you have been discriminated against.

"My biggest challenge is raising my kids to be proud of themselves and stand up for them when they are blamed for things they didn't do. My oldest is a little too smart for his britches, and I've had to step in at the school several times. I've been to the police station twice, and he has only had his license for two years.

"I have some White friends who are genuinely nice and supportive to me, but every once in a while, they talk about going to some fancy place on vacation to relax and have fun, and I wonder what that would be like. I know some White people are poor and some Blacks are rich, so it's not all because of race, but it does seem that there are more of them than there are of us. And when there is some protest or even a riot, I'm always being asked when 'your people' are going to stop causing trouble.' I don't ever hear White people asking when Whites will stop embezzling funds from their company or stop shooting up churches.

"Maybe I'm complaining too much in this video. I guess I'd just like to be respected as one woman who is trying and maybe be supported a little with raising my children to have a happy life."

"No, Latisha, we don't think you are complaining too much," said Fred. "Tony and I are just amazed at how you have kept going against all the odds. And now I want to introduce you to Bill and Marilyn Long, who will share with us their story about their experience of being Black in this city."

The camera switched over to a Black couple sitting on a couch together. They were dressed in informal clothes. Marilyn spoke for the couple.

"I remember how it felt that night when Mr. Obama was declared to have won the presidency. My husband and our two children sat with some friends in our living room, watching the returns. There was some whooping and hollering, and for a few minutes, we dared to hope that maybe our world was changing.

"Then the next day, I went to work, and one of my colleagues patted me on the back and said, 'Congratulations. Now that you've got one of your people in the White House, maybe all those Civil Rights people can take down their signs and go back to work.'

"My colleague was a nice person and good at her job, but she didn't have a clue what it would take for our society to give up being racist. All the rest of the day, many of my White colleagues would try to make jokes or cracks to their White colleagues about how they would have to watch their steps. All of it revealed how nervous they were. Later we would all experience how many White citizens were terrified with the idea that a non-White person might be making the rules. It was almost as if they knew that people of color, especially Black people, had been mistreated in this society, and now that they had someone like them in power, they would want to get their revenge.

"One of the reasons we have had so much violence and such harsh division politically in our contemporary society is that many people believe there are only winners and losers. The winners are going to take all. Wouldn't it be wonderful if our society learned to listen to each other and commit to being a team to work for a better society?

"I guess that is what our churches are trying to do by having these conversations. I just want to assure you that I believe in the same Gospel you do and that loving your neighbor doesn't stop at the color line. When I pray 'Our Father,' that means that we are all children of God, which makes us all brothers and sisters. Families have plenty of conflicts, but it can make for a beautiful family reunion when they forgive each other.

"Thank you for listening to us."

Tony's voice spoke again, "And our last speakers for this video are Felix and Barbara Armstrong from Fourth Presbyterian."

"My wife Barbara and I have really had our eyes opened by some of the recent discussions about race in our church. I'm a lawyer, and I am committed to achieving justice in our society. In my practice,

I've had to fight for equal pay for equal work and position. I've helped break racial covenants that discriminated against people living in or establishing a business in certain neighborhoods. I thought I was a liberal progressive, and I just needed to be patient for the world to catch up. It never occurred to me that what I thought was normal social mixing in our church or country club often conveyed a message of 'if you're White, you are right, but if you are Black, step back.' More than once, I watched with embarrassment when someone at the club just assumed that because someone was Black, they must be a waiter or custodian.

"I truly believe that God wants us to live in a diverse world and that everyone should have the opportunity to develop God's gifts as given them. I don't expect everyone to be geniuses, but they should feel good about themselves and be free to relate in ways that show care for their neighbor. Everyone has a gift to contribute to this society – some are stockbrokers, some landscape people, and some are inventers, but they all should have the right to develop their own talents.

"If I understand what we are trying to do as a church, we Whites must open our eyes. I confess that I am what my pastor calls a 'Recovering Racist.' Like recovering alcoholics, we are never really cured of that condition, but we can work every day to get better. For you Blacks who are watching this, I confess that I have failed you as our society has. However, if you can find it within your heart to forgive me, I will begin today to work against racism in all its forms and seek to work with you in being a better world. And Barbara shares that commitment."

Fred appeared back in the frame. "We appreciate the vulnerability that these two families from Mt. Sinai and two families from Fourth Presbyterian have shared in speaking on this video. You have also heard from Tony and me and Tyler Fisherman sharing his story from prison.

"Now, my friends, it's your turn. Along with Karen and Ezekiel, Tony and I are planning one or more evenings when we are inviting members from each of our congregations to share their stories. While we prefer to hear your public testimony, we are aware that that is difficult for many. Therefore, if you prefer and are willing to write out your story, maybe just a couple of pages long, we will arrange for them to be shared with both of our congregations.

"For Black members, we are particularly interested in hearing stories about how racism has affected your life. You might begin by sharing when you first became aware of the impact of race in your life. It may be something personal, or it may be an experience of how different businesses, schools, restaurants, etc. have treated you. Then move on through your life, noting other experiences right up to the present time. You can't tell all of them but provide us a sample, so that when all the stories are collected, we'll have a large picture of what is happening in our society."

Tony stepped up. "Let me add a couple of things. First, we'd rather hear your story then miss it because you were nervous about such things as grammar or writing style. I know of plenty of Whites and Blacks who don't consider themselves to be writers. And, if you are willing to tell your story but don't want your name on it, that's OK too. What we believe is that you will personally benefit from telling the story, and we will definitely benefit from hearing it."

Karen intervened, "Believe me, I know how nervous I got in putting this together, and I am a public speaker. What I realized is that this wasn't just sharing some information. It was sharing part of my soul. But if both of our congregations will do this, we are taking the first step to improve the world. We don't have all the details worked out yet on how the evening will go, but Ezekiel has helped us sketch out the basic framework."

Ezekiel began, "The speakers will rotate within the time framework established. Those who don't wish to speak publicly but want to tell their personal stories can write them out and read to the churches. After we have had this experience, and all who wish to speak have had their opportunity, then we will offer the opportunity for us to jointly co-write a new story as two congregations seeking to construct a vision that better reflects God's purpose for us."

Fred intervened. "We will begin that process with another survey sent to each of our congregations. While we expect that each congregation will still have a distinct perspective because of their backgrounds, it will be interesting to see how having had this video experience together will affect how we respond to the survey. Once we've received your responses, our college friends, Fran and her colleagues, will tabulate your answers and prepare a summary of each congregation's self-understanding. We are fully aware that within any congregation, there will be a variety of responses. Still, we will share the predominant response to each of the questions with you so that you can grasp both the challenge and the promise that your church offers."

"Let me reinforce that issue of diversity," said Tony. "I have frequently been asked, 'what do Black people want, particularly Black Christians?' Having been a pastor for a couple of decades, I can assure you that there is as much diversity among Black people as there is among White people. We are all over the place.

"Even saying that we all belong to Christ doesn't eliminate the diversity among us. The value of the surveys is to provide us with an approximate picture of where our churches stand as we proceed with our conversation."

"Gee," said Fred, "You sound like you are describing a group of White Christians. I guess we are going to have to confront this challenge by really learning to listen to each other."

"I knew you would get that listening bit in here somewhere," laughed Tony. "But that is the value of our making use of these surveys. They provide us with a picture of each of our congregations. Tony and I will arrange a large meeting and celebration of our congregations together. We'll have time for questions and answers, time for listening not only to each other but together listening to God."

"I'm asking each of you to watch for your survey on an email, and if you prefer to have a physical copy, call your church office," said Fred. "Fill it out, and then, when Fran and her colleagues have summarized the responses from each of our churches, look for your invitation to our two-church banquet."

"And thanks," added Tony, "for committing to join in this exciting adventure with each other and with the Christ who invites us to be learners or disciples of his love."

"Wow," said Lilly after the camera had turned off, looking at Ariel, "I wonder what our husbands have got us into? Do you suppose the two congregations will really listen and respond?"

"Since we are both pastor's wives," Ariel said, "the one thing we both have experienced is that you never know what we are about to experience."

**FOR CHAPTER RESOURCES AND ADDITIONAL CONTENT, SCAN THIS QR CODE:**

SMcCutchan.Kartra.com/page/CHAPTER26

# CHAPTER 27

# THE THIRD ROUND OF QUESTIONS

Alice straightened up her desk as she waited for Fred to arrive. She had watched different churches be ripped apart as they attempted to respond to volatile issues in society. She was concerned after Fred preached his sermon on racism back near Pentecost. She knew the sermon came out of the pool of pain that he felt when pastor Southgate's son was shot. And she marveled at how frequently in the past few weeks it looked like they were headed for an eruption. Then, at the last moment, an unexpected event interrupted and opened up a promising new direction.

She was blown away when she watched the video that they had put together. The laypeople who spoke from both congregations were powerful. She had been at Fourth for ten years, and she had never witnessed that level of excitement and nervousness before. Over the years, she had made friends with many church members. Some of them loved to exchange gossip about what was happening. Her phone had been ringing off the wall since the video had been put up on the church website.

Fred walked through the door and greeted her with a wide smile. "Well, Miss Outsider-with-all-the-inside-information, what is the word on the gossip line?"

"I'm somewhat amazed at how energized people were in response to the video," said Alice. "Of course, we are still tiptoeing up to the central issue of racism. Karen tells me that both Fourth and Mt. Sinai will send this next survey out to each of your congregations and gauge where each congregation is. I know that the two churches are beginning to have a good relationship, as seen in that video, but their views on race are bound to be different."

"Of course they will be," said Fred, "but that is part of the point." He moved towards his desk and picked up a paper copy of the survey to be sent out. "Fran and her friends are going to summarize the answers from each church. Then we will share them at a special banquet."

"That might be a little touchy when each church sees how the other church views this. If they are honest, Black people and White people just don't view racism in the same way."

"We're not asking them to agree. We're asking them to listen to each other."

"Oh, that scuche thing you are always talking about."

"Escúcheme, yes. And I hope we have some guidelines that will help them with that. Let me test this out with you. Everyone will have a copy of Fran's summary and will see the differences. We'll have a couple of new speakers in the same format as was seen on the video.

As they read the graphs and listen to the videos, we will remind them that we are observing a cumulative response and not the opinions of individuals. Then we will open the floor for comments. In good Active Listening fashion, as a person rises to speak, we ask them to comment on what they have heard, either positive or negative and the feelings that they read into what they have heard. The next speaker must first summarize what they have heard and only when they have heard accurately, can they add their own comments.

We will acknowledge that this can become frustrating, but we are asking them to listen in a focused way. If someone feels their opinions are not being voiced, we will create space for them to speak as well.

"That's going to take a little getting used to. We normally try to make comments to communicate our response, not show we understand the other person. I think you would help the process if you had a printed script that frames the way you want people to respond."

Karen entered the office area and heard what they were talking about. "Yeah, if we had a small paper in big print that said, 'As I read this part of the summary,' and then quote the part, 'I hear these feelings behind those thoughts.' Is that right?"

"That sounds good, but it will probably become clearer once we see Fran's summaries," said Fred. "If it is possible, both Tony and I would like to get the surveys out today and give them about three days to mark their responses and return them. Since we are using Survey Monkey, we can permit Fran to access the responses and begin to build the graphs for each congregation." He turned to Alice. "Does that seem workable?"

"My part is easy. It's you two and Reverend Southgate who have to deal with any blowback."

"Great. Karen, why don't you and I review where we are, and hopefully where we are going. We'll let Alice get busy with the mailing."

Fred and Karen grabbed a cup of coffee and went into Fred's office. As they did, Fred began, "I think you and Zeke did a fantastic job for the video. The way things have been going, I think we should get a good response from both congregations."

"I do too, but that creates another problem."

Fred took a sip of coffee. "I think I know where you are going but tell me."

"We have a congregation of about 600 members, and Tony's church is about 300. Let's say about half of them get so excited about what's happening that they show up for the banquet. How do we get 500 people to interact around a touchy subject like this constructively?"

"I've been thinking about that. Both you and Alice suggested a written guideline for their responses. With a little introduction and maybe even some group rehearsal, I think we can shape how they respond."

"And could we make certain in some way that they all sit in small mixed groups? Then they could practice what we are striving for between the two churches. And maybe we could do that while they are eating. Food often helps keep the conversation flowing."

Fred picked up a tablet and began making notes. "After an hour or so, we could ask them to frame some ideas that we could explore together as congregations. As each small group leader shares their ideas, we could practice active listening and keep a list of what is suggested on an overhead for later exploration."

"I like it. They are working together as teams, experience being taken seriously, and become even more invested in moving ahead."

"Tony and I have talked about how we respond if we run into difficult responses and argumentative individuals."

"I'd suggest that you engage them with active listening and add them to the list. You are good at that, and it would demonstrate exactly what you have been urging."

"Does it make you nervous, wondering how people will respond to this survey?" asked Fred.

"Of course, it does, but I think somewhere Jesus advised us not to worry about tomorrow because we have enough to worry about today. That's something we can do something about. For example, where are we going to find a place to have this banquet that we can both have small groups but also hear each other as a whole group?"

"Ever the practical one," said Fred as he shook his head. "Okay, captain, let's get to working on today's issues, but I'll still be nervous until I see Fran's summaries."

**FOR CHAPTER RESOURCES AND ADDITIONAL CONTENT, SCAN THIS QR CODE:**
SMcCutchan.Kartra.com/page/CHAPTER27

# CHAPTER 28

# THE SUMMARIES COME IN

Two weeks after the surveys went out to the two congregations, Fran asked if she could meet with Fred, Tony, and Karen to discuss the returns. They agreed to meet at Tony's church at 4 p.m. on Tuesday.

Tuesday afternoon, Fred turned on Phillip's Avenue and drove down three blocks before rounding a curve and saw Mt. Sinai before him. It was an attractive, large A-frame brick building centered on a beautifully landscaped plot in a residential neighborhood. It was clear that the trustees took pride in the building and the land around the church.

Extending out to the left of the building was an office suite and a small parking lot. Fred parked his car near where a sign hung indicating the entrance to the offices. He and Tony agreed that he would come a half-hour early to review some details about the upcoming banquet. They were excited to discover that a high percentage of the members responded quickly.

Fran was linked into the site, so she also saw the responses as they came in. She had reported that she and her classmates had quickly organized the responses into some charts that they could review. The last they had spoken, she noted that she already had between three and four hundred responses. He hated to say he was grateful for the hostage experience. Still, he recognized that the publicity around that incident had created enough interest that their membership was eager to tune in either to the live event or the video they had posted on their respective church sites.

As he entered the office suite, he quickly spotted Tony emerging from the sanctuary hallway with his arm around a couple of members. He was calmly speaking to them as if it were a pastoral moment, so Fred moved quietly to the large windows that revealed the office suite. The secretary greeted Fred, "Dr. Southgate will be with you directly. Would you like a cup of coffee while you wait?"

"It's been a long afternoon. A cup of coffee, black, sounds great. I saw Dr. Southgate with a couple in the hall, so I know he is aware of my presence."

He thought about the large lounge they had reserved for the coming celebration. Tony had made the reservation at a private women's club nearby. From Tony's description, it would be large enough for multiple round tables of eight, all facing a stage with several mikes for easy communication. As he reviewed some pictures that Tony had snapped of the banquet hall on his iPhone, he thought of the media consultant from his church who had offered to supply some battery mikes to place on the individual tables.

As he was musing on these events, Tony came through the door. "Isn't ministry wonderful?" said Tony. "This morning I helped welcome the birth of a new life into this world, and just now, I think some active listening and soulful prayer may have begun a process of healing for a troubled couple."

"Those are some of the moments that sustain us when the stress of other events seems about to overwhelm us," responded Fred.

"Okay," said Tony, "I just confirmed the reservation for our joint celebration. Fran messaged me that she was now up to 450 responses. Is this really happening, or am I just dreaming?"

"What other details do we need to tie down?" asked Fred.

They were chatting about various details when the office door opened, and a cheery Fran Smith almost waltzed into the office suite. "Hi, pastors. You won't believe what I've got to show you."

"Tony tells me you are up to 450 responses now."

"That was a half-hour ago. Now I just topped 500, and since I'm using Survey Monkey, I only have to punch a button and out pops a graph of the responses." She opened her backpack and pulled out a set of files. "Boy, you two pastors have fabulous congregations. Wait till you see these."

Fred could feel the excitement building as he glanced at the graphs on the papers before him.

"I'm not sure how you will use these, but you have some good data on your congregations. When I showed these to one of my professors, he got so excited I thought for a moment he was going to leap over his desk and hug me. I may not want that –he's a little old and out of shape to interest me, but it wouldn't hurt my GPA to get a good grade from this class."

Mt. Airy -- Dark Grey / Fourth – Light Grey

    A.        An Overworked Complaint of Liberals

B.      Invisible Reality that Distorts Society

C.      A Harmful Condition affecting all Black Citizens.

D.      A Challenge that if Understood could Heal our Divided Society.

Tony said, "These look great." He leafed through the stack of papers. "The neat part about what you have here is that it shows both the diversity and the similarity of our congregations. I don't see any of the questions that didn't have some people from each congregation choose each of the choices." He shook his head, "Yet for the life of me, I can't understand how some of my people chose some of these choices."

"Wouldn't it be interesting to explore as a group why different people made their choices?" said Fred. "Look at question #4. I find it hopeful that both congregations recognize the power of guilt to set back these conversations and mix those from Mt. Sinai who believe it will never change with those from Fourth who think we are making progress. If we can learn to actively listen to each other, that provides ample material to advance our conversation."

"What I don't quite understand is how you are going to get over 600 people to engage in that conversation," said Fran.

"Fred and I have been kicking that around," said Tony. "Let me describe our idea and tell me what you think about it."

Fran held up her hand. "Wait a second while I get my laptop out to take some notes." She reached back into her backpack and pulled out a mini-laptop and set it up. "Okay, I'm listening."

"Well, first of all," said Tony, "We've arranged for a large banquet hall over at the Women's Recreation Center on Klondike street on Saturday evening, October 1."

Fred jumped in. "They have a large banquet hall that can hold at least 75 round tables, each of which can seat eight, and if necessary, there is a spillover room that could hold up to twenty more tables. There is a front stage and a good sound system that also could be piped into the spillover room. And it is also set up so that we could stream it to our churches' websites for those who want to hear but not attend."

"And," Tony continued, "you have just expanded our reach by making up these charts. As we are speaking, we can project each of the questions onto a screen so that we are all seeing the same question together."

"I can see that, but how do you shape the conversation so that the loudest voice doesn't dominate?" asked Fran. "I've seen those large assemblies at my school, not even this large. Usually, a few people dominate, and lots of us just sit back and let them take over."

"You probably have more experience at this," said Fred, "but how does this sound? First, when people arrive, we make sure that all tables have a racial mix. Then, when we show a question on the screen, we begin by pointing out the dominant responses from each congregation, and we ask each table first to discuss what they see and second to discuss as a table how they would like their congregations to respond to deepen our understanding of racism in our churches."

"That's neat, but remember you still have at least 75 table groups, which takes quite a lot of time to report in."

"She's got a point," said Fred. "75 report outs would get repetitive and less interesting. You do that for seven questions, and it doesn't leave any time for discussion."

"If we can find the funds, I think my techie-husband might be able to help us out," said Karen.

"What's that?" asked Tony.

"He once worked at a convention, and they had this large banquet with people in small groups, some even in different rooms. We make sure that each table has someone with a cell phone. Using a program like menti.com, we can interact with all the tables, allowing them to have table votes and identify questions they would like to raise for the entire body. We can provide each table a voting remote that allows people to register their table vote They can also post questions their table has for the whole group."

"Zowie!" said Tony. "We are going high tech."

"If we record it all," said Fran, "and I have some of my colleagues also keep notes, we'd have a way to provide them a summary later."

"To bring it back to the human side," said Karen, "we could have a couple of people from each congregation do a quick sort of summary statement of what they have heard and then conclude with some communal singing and litany prayers."

"It sounds almost too good to be true, and it might be. How do we prepare if some individual or group comes prepared to challenge what we are doing and throw an adversarial wrench into our plans?" asked Fran.

"I asked that same question," said Tony, "and I think Karen suggested the right approach. This whole project has been built on the mantra summed up by that Spanish word 'escúcheme.' if someone does become disruptive, we try our best to actively listen to their comments and feelings and make a note of them as we proceed with our process."

"I've got a lot of cynical friends who don't believe we will ever get past these racial divisions," said Fran. "I think if they could see this, it might break through some of their skepticism. It might even make them reconsider their faith. It certainly has caused me to take a second look."

 **FOR CHAPTER RESOURCES AND ADDITIONAL CONTENT, SCAN THIS QR CODE:**
SMcCutchan.Kartra.com/page/CHAPTER28

# CHAPTER 29

# THE CELEBRATION CONVERSATION

The Presbytery had consulted with Fred and Tony and were going to have some members there to observe. They had gotten excited about the process and even had some inquiries from the General Assembly. The reporters who had been present at the Jimmy's Mini Mart store had kept track of how events had unfolded. Even the mayor of the city had asked to be kept up to date.

Fred, Tony, Karen, and Fran arrived at the Burger King near the banquet hall on Saturday at about 11:30. They had agreed that gathering for a quick lunch and then heading over to the women's club by about one would allow them to review details and make sure that everything was set for people to arrive about seven that evening.

"This is probably overkill," said Fred as he joined Tony in line, "but I won't relax this afternoon anyway, and we might as well make sure everything is in order."

"I'm with you there," said Tony. "I see that Fran and Karen have already snagged a table for us."

Once they had their orders, they took them to the table where Karen and Fran were chatting and sipping a drink.

"Heh, guys, good to see you. Fran was just telling me that she thinks the whole campus is abuzz about our event. Makes me a little nervous. I believe in our plan, but it scares me to think what will happen if this messes up."

"Can't let that happen," says Fran. "You people only have to worry about your career and reputation, but my grade is riding on this. By the way," she turned to Tony, "I did get that recording equipment that you asked for. It's in the car. And Zeke will meet us at the club about three to help set up the voting machines at each table."

"Karen, you checked on the greeters from both churches and the color-coded placemats that will be at each table?"

"Copacetic," said Karen. "Color coding the placemats according to the graph colors for each church was a clever idea. I delivered them to the club before I came here. I also gave them the packet of graphs, and they will put eight of them on each table."

"Do you really think over six hundred people will show up for this on a Saturday night?" asked Fran.

"Between the two congregations, we had that many reservations. Can't say we get that type of attendance at worship on Sundays, but the excitement over this is pretty high," said Tony.

They continued to chat and share nervous laughter as they ate their sandwiches until about one, and then they parted with Tony and Fred heading over to the club.

People started coming shortly after 6 p.m. The greeters explained that they were to find their places from the seating chart and look for their nametag at the appropriate table. The food selection they had selected when they made their reservation had been given to the catering group prepared to serve them rapidly beginning at 7 p.m.

A quartet offered them a singing grace promptly at seven, and they were urged to both eat and get acquainted with the others at their table. A member from each table had been contacted ahead of time and instructed about using the hand-held mike and voting machine at each table.

Tony and Fred greeted the crowd after the quartet had finished. Then, Fred explained, "Your food is being delivered, and we encourage you to use the next thirty minutes or so to enjoy your food and get acquainted with those at your table. Then we will convene you as a group. I'll ask Dr. Southgate to offer a prayer for this food and this evening."

Tony stepped forward. "Please take ahold of the hands next to you and let us pray." Following the prayer, there was a comfortably loud chatter as people ate and conversed around their respective tables.

At about 7:35, Fred asked for their attention. "You will notice at each of your tables a set of seven graphs reflecting the responses of each of our congregations to the survey we sent out. Please pass them around so that each person has a copy. We will look at the first three questions as a set together.

Mt. Sinai-- Light Grey / Fourth—Dark Grey

A: Makes White People Defensive

B: Makes Black People Angry

C: A Temptation to Misuse Power

D. An Opportunity to be a Blessing to Others.

Mt. Sinai is light grey / Fourth is Dark Grey

    A. The guilt that White people feel.

    B. Black people's belief that nothing will ever change.

    C. Feeling helpless to solve an historic injustice.

    D. Fear of stirring up conflict among people.

Mt. Airy -- Dark Grey / Fourth – Light Grey

    A.       An Overworked Complaint of Liberals

    B.       Invisible Reality that Distorts Society

    C.       A Harmful Condition affecting all Black Citizens.

    D.       A Challenge that if Understood could Heal our Divided Society.

Fred continued, "You will notice on question one that our congregations, while holding differing opinions on what they think about talking about racism, are surprisingly similar in the way they break down their responses."

Tony spoke up, "While we are in general agreement that such a conversation can be difficult for both of our congregations, there is a high percentage of both of our congregations who believe that the opportunity for healing of our society can benefit from these conversations -- which is why we are here.

"When we get to question #2, you will notice two things. First, almost half of each of our congregations believe that White guilt is a major barrier to those conversations. Where the two congregations most contrast is that the next most common answer from Mt. Sinai was that nothing will ever change. While the second most common answer at Fourth was that we are slowly making progress and just need to be patient."

However, you will notice when you look at Question #3, the vast majority of Fourth Church believes that racism is a reality that is harmful to all Black citizens. A large proportion of Mt. Sinai agrees that racism distorts our whole society."

Fred came back to the mike. "So, you are not that far apart in recognizing that though it is a difficult conversation to have, it offers us an opportunity to heal the types of divisions we all have witnessed here in the city and across our country. We would like you to take those three graphs and engage in what we call active listening.

"You will see in the back of your packet a little guideline for how that takes place. You are going to be discussing two topics.

"First, what is the overall message you hear from what I just shared with you, and how does it make you feel as a Black person or a White person? And when someone shares, the next person to respond first tries to reflect both what the previous person is saying and the feelings underneath that; only then does the next person add what they want to say. The process repeats itself -- first reflect what you've heard and then share your response.

"As a group, keep searching for something you would like your two churches to do that might have positive results. After about one-half hour, we will ask the spokesperson from each table to type their table's suggestion into the voting machine."

Fran was backstage making all sorts of yips and squeals as she read the different suggestions come in. Right before Fred was about to introduce the second set of questions, Fran came on stage and whispered into Fred's ear. Fred then spoke, "Ladies and gentlemen, if you don't know her, I have with me Fran Smith, who is the one assisting us by writing up the survey results in a somewhat coherent fashion. She would like to have a brief word before we proceed. Fran, the mike is yours."

Fran approached the mike. She was dressed in slacks and a bright blouse. She had let her hair go natural and beamed with confidence.

"Hi," she said. "As Pastor Fred explained, "I'm the data collector for your surveys. You have a lot of work to do, so I'll just take a moment. Tonight, I've been reading through the various suggestions you have been making. I truly believe that if I could describe what these two congregations are doing to the students at my college, you'd suddenly have a lot of college visitors at your churches.

"Many of my classmates used to go to church but have dropped out since they came to college. They are generally cynical about the church in general, saying that the Gospel might be okay and they like Jesus, but they see churches as filled with members who are afraid to live the Gospel.

"Some of your suggestions reflect your uneasiness about getting involved, but all of them show two churches that are not afraid to trust God enough to give it a try. Thank you for giving me the chance to observe you and your efforts to love justice, do kindness, and have enough courage to try to walk humbly with God. I can't wait to see what you do in response to the next set of questions." Then with a slight bow, she withdrew from the stage.

"Thank you, Fran. I might tell the rest of you that Fran and some friends have done a great deal of work these past few months to help us out. In fact, one of her professors has asked her to write this event up, and he will submit it to one of his religious journals -- names redacted, of course.

Tony turned back to his handouts. "The next two questions, number 5 and 6, deal with our feelings and perceptions about the color of our skins. Let's try a little something different. In this next set of questions, we are dealing with our perception of what it is like to have White or Black skin and live in this society. But instead of sharing our own experiences as we have seen in the video stories, let us begin by first sharing what we think the others would say. Try to respond to the questions as if you were the other person's race. I've put the survey questions in your packet without any scores. Instead of voting for yourself, try to imagine how the majority of the other congregation would vote. Then, using your table voting machine, report your tables vote.

Once your table has collected these votes, share the feelings that you have about that vote. How accurate do you think people's assumptions about the other congregations were?

Once we gather all the tables scores in, you may want to share some opinions about future events that we might have that address how accurately we see each other.

Again, there was a rumble of conversation, occasionally interrupted with some laughter or cheers. The reports came in through the voting machines, and everyone watched as the graph finally filled up. While they were dealing with a serious subject, occasionally, there was good-natured kidding and some general relaxing of tension.

"Now," said Karen, "we come to our final set of two questions. They deal with two serious aspects of being Black in our society. Both the economic reality and the population of our prisons is based on what our research has shown as reliable statistics.

"First, share how the members at your table react to these two realities. Then, having shared your reactions, brainstorm together what ministries our churches might undertake which, while not completely resolving the disparities, could both recognize the reality and begin small steps our respective congregations could take together to make a difference. Again, you only have a half-hour, and you can't solve these complex problems in this short time, but you can identify some small steps we could take. And as you brainstorm possible steps, don't forget to actively listen to each other."

About a half-hour later, Tony, recognizing the intense conversations taking place, announced that they would have fifteen more minutes, and then they would be asked to report their conclusions. After fifteen more minutes, he spoke. "I know that many of you are still working intensely, but we have been at this for almost three hours. We will take your suggestions, and we will form some bi-church task forces and return the results to you."

Aaron Craddock interrupted Tony's speech and asked to be recognized. Fred knew Aaron, who intermittently came to church but was frequently out of town on business. While no one knew for sure, it was rumored that he was a multi-millionaire. "I ask you to forgive me, Reverend Southgate, and you too, Reverend Livinggood, but before you dismiss these fine people who have worked so hard tonight, I would like to add a personal response."

He approached the stage even as Fred was trying to prepare how to handle the situation.

"My name is Aaron Craddock, and I am a somewhat irregular member of Fourth Presbyterian. I am a successful multi-millionaire businessman who is accustomed to intimidating others rather than being intimidated by them." He paused and glanced at Fred. "In fact, I've even tried to intimidate Pastor Livinggood a few times, although I must admit I haven't been very successful at it, especially lately."

There was some nervous laughter that rippled through the audience, but also, it was clear that he had their full attention.

"I was one of the members of Fourth Church who objected to our getting involved in this whole discussion of race and racism and even threatened to withhold my pledge if it continued. I was of the mindset that money was one of the ways to make sure people did what I wanted."

"However, I also have always prided myself in having the strength to listen to those who thought differently than I did. Often that has been the source of new ideas and innovations that have made me successful. Therefore, in the past few months, I have done three things that are unusual for me. First, I've attended church faithfully.

Second, I've tried to really listen to what Fred was saying. Third, I've often been furious when, in essence, he told me I was a racist and I'd better wake up and smell the coffee."

"Did you learn anything?" a voice shouted out from the audience.

There was a brief silence, and then Aaron said, "Yes, I did. One of the things I learned was the power of what he calls active listening. And whoever yelled that out, I challenge you to join me on the stage and let us practice listening to each other in front of this gathering of our church members."

There was a sharp intake of breath throughout all those gathered. Then there was a rustle about two-thirds of the way back in the banquet hall. A large powerfully built man rose from a table and began to move towards the stage. As he walked, there was the sound of supportive applause that rippled through the people and a few shouts of 'speak the truth,' 'truth to power,' and 'way to go, man.'

Tony whispered to Fred, "Meredith is a former pro-football player. He's a strong voice in Mt. Sinai but not always very cooperative. I think I'm about to test out the effectiveness of prayer."

"I'm with you, brother, but if this is to work, we need to listen to strong voices, so maybe this can have some good results."

Meredith made it up the stairs to the stage. He met Aaron in the middle of the stage and shook his hand. They exchanged names. Both gave the appearance of not being intimidated by the other.

Aaron spoke first. "Many of you may already know Meredith Dickerson, and I think you should appreciate his willingness to speak up." He turned to Meredith and continued, "What I heard from your comment from the audience is that you wondered if this was just one more White guy throwing his weight around to get noticed and you were skeptical whether this was all going to end with a bunch of useless words." He then looked at Meredith for a response.

Meredith chuckled and leaned toward the mike, "Just to level the playing field a little, many of you may not know, but I played pro-football for about eight years. I, too, made a lot of money. I was also the president of the players union and mixed with a lot of rich people in negotiating for the players, so I'm not a stranger to powerful people trying to impose their will on others."

"And your initial evaluation of what you've heard from me?" Aaron asked.

"I learned you are strong enough to invite me up on this stage and speak face to face. That shows some courage that I respect," said Meredith.

"So, let me tell you another thing about me, and I believe a lot of White people, Meredith. I guarantee I wouldn't have said this before the events of these past couple of months, but I think both Black and White churches are victims of this thing called racism. We need to stop hiding from each other and face our reality."

"That sounds good, but a couple of evenings of conversation ain't going to change the facts. Every day Emily and I, and millions of Black people who are a lot poorer and more powerless than we are, have to rise every morning wondering how to teach our children to be proud of themselves even though the world thinks they are inferior."

There was not a sound in the audience as they waited for Aaron to respond.

"I can't change that, Meredith, but I can begin with this group tonight to call a lie a lie and work to begin to repair some of the damage that has been done. I also have the resources, admittedly secured from an unjust society, to begin to invite others into a conversation about how we can build a more just world."

"So, you going to pay back the Black community all the money you stole from them in this crooked society."

"I hear you saying that you are furious that even though you made a lot of money because of your physical skills, because the White community was willing to pay to see you play, you and your Black neighbors every day have to live in an unfair world."

"You are right there. We deserve some reparations."

"You are right, and I confess to you that I'm too big a coward to give up my wealth and become poor because I took advantage of a society built in my favor. There is no set of actions that I can take that will reform the world, but I am willing to take some action to move in the right direction. As you learned in your negotiations with the Players Union, sometimes you only make slow progress, but each success builds on the one before it."

"I'm listening."

"Let's start with our churches and the churches they are connected with."

"What have you got in mind?"

"We need to keep going what has happened in our churches and invite other churches to join us in building a vision of what our society could look like if we just learned to listen to each other. I was very moved by the stories that were told in the video, and I don't want to lose them."

"They were powerful, but powerful stories have been told before and just listening to each other isn't going to make the world fairer."

"OK, but let's preserve the stories that these churches possess. I think we have something unique here. What if we invite any members of these churches to tell their stories? Black volunteers can share what it is like to be Black in our society and what it takes to both survive and prepare their children to survive. White members will share what they have learned about how they benefit from and participate in our society's racial structures and commit to at least one thing they will do to help support the church in building a vision of a better world. When we collect these testimonies, I will have them published as a book and will buy a copy for every member of our two churches."

Tony interrupted, "I think Fred and I could add another dimension to this. If you could see your way to purchase another couple of hundred copies, we could make sure that every church in our Presbytery gets a copy if they promise to share and discuss the book in their church."

"I'm not sure how long this book might get, but either as part of the book or as an extra, Tony and I could prepare a guide for how any of our churches could duplicate our experience and see if they can create their church's own book describing where the Gospel is being fleshed out in our admittedly racist society," added Fred.

"Another member from the audience stood up. "If you get that book published, I'll buy a series of copies and share them with some of my business colleagues and see if they are part of religious communities who might participate."

Several other tables started talking about what they could do. Another speaker at another table stood up. "Our pastors are always reminding us that the transformation of the world began in a small stable in an out of the way village in what the Romans saw as a third-rate country." There was a round of applause.

Tony spoke up, "Maybe our effort to heal the racial splits and honor our diversity begins here. Whether it happens or not is up to God but whether we try or not is up to us."

Suddenly the door at the rear of the stage was flung open. The sound was loud enough to draw the attention of many near the front of the crowd. The attention of people was drawn towards a wheelchair being pushed through the door. In the chair was a frail-looking Black youth with a big smile on his face. Behind the chair was Ariel Southgate and Lilly Livinggood. They moved towards the mike at the center while Tony and Fred rushed to assist.

Tony spoke in a voice filled with emotion. "Ladies and gentlemen, this is my son, Eric, who was shot by the city police four months ago. Thanks be to God; he is recovering slowly."

Ariel stepped up to the mike. "He can't say much yet, but a lot of what is happening here tonight had its origin as a result of that shooting and Fred and Tony's response. The shooting was unjustified, but it is a living witness to what God can do with horrible acts to invite us to experience a transformed society."

Eric signaled he wanted the mike. In a raspy voice, he said, "Because of the bullet, I may be a cripple the rest of my life, but if because of that bullet, life gets better for several hundred people in these churches, then instead of anger, I'll feel it was worth it."

 **FOR CHAPTER RESOURCES AND ADDITIONAL CONTENT, SCAN THIS QR CODE:**

SMcCutchan.Kartra.com/page/CHAPTER29

# CHAPTER 30

# TELLING A NEW STORY

"It's just hard for me to comprehend what has happened in the past few months," said Fred. "This whole series of events that have led us to this moment, they could have been derailed so many times, and yet weren't."

Karen opened a laptop and typed a few words before she said, "I know we have to begin sketching out how our guidebook will look, but it may also be an excellent time to reflect on the significance of those events. I'm not one for thinking this way, but it does cause you to wonder what God has in mind for the church?"

"I preach about how God transformed the world by beginning with a small event like the birth of an unknown baby, but that was theology in sermons. Now I start to wonder if something significant is going to begin right here in our little church. Let's pause a moment and think about this," said Fred. "What do you realistically think might happen as a result of all of this? First, what's the worst that can happen?"

"I think that the worst that could happen is that we had some excellent exchanges with Mt. Sinai, and all of us have grown a little. Racism is a horrible plague on our society, and we have made a little dent in it," said Karen. "Ezekiel took me in his arms after we got home and said, 'We've actually had some honest talk about race and racism. I never expected that from a White church. Thanks for helping me believe in miracles.' If all we got out of this adventure was that moment, I'd have said all my work on this has been worthwhile."

"Lilly was very affectionate after we got home as well. Who knew that talking about racism could be like an aphrodisiac? But after that, she also asked what I was going to do if the General Assembly or even other denominations were to ask us to help them start a similar conversation."

"I guess what we've learned is that we are not in charge of what will happen. All we are in charge of is being as faithful as we can and see what happens," Karen said.

"What are some of the points we want in a guidebook?"

"I think that all those sermons you've preached on how God has a habit of working with imperfect churches to accomplish miraculous things could help a church move past the fear of making mistakes so they can take small steps in faith and listen for God's guidance."

"And maybe, since most members in our churches would like to move past racism and its destructive results, maybe we could offer some steps to take that would help a church begin to build a vision of where we are headed. You know, little steps that not only advance us but deepen our faith as well. What might a church liberated from racism look like?" pondered Fred.

"And what if we developed some liturgical resources that would enable Christians to praise God for whatever progress is made. That helps remind us that this is more than an extra action but is central to our faith journey?

Then," Karen continued, "We need to drill down on how to listen to each other actively and to the stranger who shows up in our life."

"We also need to help them begin to build a relationship with Christians of other cultures. We need to help them discover the richness of diversity in God's universe," said Fred.

"We also need to help them understand that anywhere there is a hiccup in the process, rather than see this as a failure, it needs to be an opportunity to listen deeply to what God is saying to us. Escúcheme applies to whole churches as well."

The door to the office opened, and Lilly and Ezekiel walked in. "Hear the Word of the Lord," Ezekiel intoned.

"You are to stop work right now and take your spouses to a fine restaurant," added Lilly.

"I'd like to do that, but we have a lot of work to do," said Fred.

"Escúcheme" said Lilly and Ezekiel in harmony, "It is time to celebrate and to trust."

"I believe," said Karen with a nod, "that I've just experienced a thin moment and we had better listen."

 **FOR CHAPTER RESOURCES AND ADDITIONAL CONTENT, SCAN THIS QR CODE:**
SMcCutchan.Kartra.com/page/CHAPTER30

# AFTERWORD

This story is fiction, but I believe that that it is a story that reflects real possibilities in churches that sincerely want to address the issue of racism in our society. In the early part of 2021, I will have constructed two non-fiction booklets that provide step-by-step instructions for how both congregations and judicatories can develop an anti-racist strategy for their ministries. You will be able to find them at my website, www.smccutchan.com. I would especially draw your attention to RACISM AND GOD'S GRACE: Truth and Reconciliation for the American Church, published in February 2021. That is also where you will find my twice-weekly blogs that address various aspects of ministry and ways to keep both ministry and churches healthy.

You can find a description of all of my publications at my website: www.smccutchan.com or by looking me up on Amazon.

If I can help answer any questions, address your leadership group, or advance the cause of developing strategies to address racism in a creative way, you may contact me at steve@smccutchan.com.

On the next three pages are some suggested questions especially for a clergy study group gathered to discuss Shock and Awe. While the story can raise plenty of questions worthy of discussion, these questions guide the group in exploring the possibility of a constructive anti-racism ministry in their churches. Choose some clergy friends who might benefit from such an exploration.

# QUESTIONS FOR REFLECTION
## Study Group

Chapter 1: The Reception Line:
1. Have you ever witnessed such a confrontation after worship?
2. How do you respond to Victor's comment re 'your people'?

Chapter 2: Putting Flesh on Spoken Words:
1. What do you learn about tension in Black families from the lunch conversation?
2. What pressures do pastors experience to preach so not to upset people?

Chapter 3: Our Brother:
1. How do you react to the scene at the hospital?
2. How would you react if it were your child, and how does race factor in?

Chapter 4: Be Angry, But Don't Let the Sun Go Down:
1. What do you think of Ariel's question about God working for good?
2. Do Whites fear Black retaliation if they ever get the power? (36)

Chapter 5: Not All Sermons are the Same:

1. Do White parents assume that society's structures are geared to keep them safe while Black parents have to warn about the dangers of these same structures? (40)
2. How do you react to Tony's rejection of Fred's offer to preach for him? (42)

Chapter 6: Threaten the pastor:

1. How frequently do you think pastors are threatened in their ministry?
2. Discuss Fred's analogy between Alcoholics Anonymous and facing racism.

Chapter 7: A Guilty Wall:

1. React to David and Fred's talk about how Jesus would respond.
2. What do you think is proper relation of church and state in society?

Chapter 8: Lilly:

1. What are the pressures on pastor's wives?
2. Is 'What would Jesus have the church do?' a good question to discuss?

Chapter 9 Escúcheme:
1. What is your reaction to the comments about Escúcheme?
2. How do you understand the phrase "Thin Moment"?

Chapter 10: The Seeds of a Plan
1. What is value of a congregation-wide conversation using technology?
2. Does "God call people to a particular church for a reason? How does it make you feel to personally consider that?

Chapter 11: Church Business and Peacemaking:
1. What are the reasons for Fred arranging the conversation among Victor, Fran, and David?
2. How does that reflect Fred's understanding of the church?

Chapter 12: Living with Guilt:
1. How do you react to Fran's description of how young people view the church?
2. How do you react to Fran's description of what she needs in a church? (100)

Chapter 13: Imperfect Church:
1. How effective do you think the demonstration of 'Active Listening' among the session is?
2. What would be the impact if a whole church learned to listen deeply to each other?

Chapter 14: The Sermon Proposal:
1. Do pastors see the wounds among the membership as they stand before a congregation?
2. What do you think of Fred's assertion that conflict can be a space for blessing?

Chapter 15: Thin Moments:
1. What do you think of the 'Wilderness" metaphor for today's churches?
2. What would be some of the snakes encountered if a church addresses racism?

Chapter 16: A Wilderness Journey:
1. What would be the value of a whole church conversing about God's call for the church?
2. How do you react to using the multiple-choice format for engaging the congregation?

Chapter 17: A Meal to Relax:
1. Does racism contribute to more health problems for Black people?
2. How do you react to Ariel's comment about the emotional toll of always being tense?

Chapter 18: Truth and Reconciliation:

1. How do you describe the difference between personal and institutional racism?

2. How do you understand the of Truth and Reconciliation process?

Chapter 19: An Uncertain Vision:

1. How close would your congregation agree with the graph?

2. Do you think the sequence of the questions Karen proposes would enable a church to build a fair image of who they were as a church? Would that be helpful?

Chapter 20: Engaging the Congregation:

1. Do you think the series of questions can help a church hear God?

2. How do you react to the interaction between Victor and Martha?

Chapter 21: Taking A Hostage:

1. Is Tony's experience in the factory a common life experience for Black laborers?

2. What caused the reduction of tension in the store?

Chapter 22: Leaders Are Servants:
1. How do you understand the power issue as it affects their joint church conversation?
2. Do you think the video is a good way to introduce the churches to the process?

Chapter 23: Trust and Obey:
1. How do you understand Tutu's idea about forgiveness?
2. What does the interview with Tyler contribute to the experience?

Chapter 24: A Model of Forgiveness:
1. Is the interaction with Tony an illustration for how God can work good out of evil?
2. Does it make you think of someone to whom you need to deeply listen?

Chapter 25: My Story, Your Story:
1. How does Ariel's example of disciples becoming vulnerable strike you? (246)
2. How do you understand the term 'servant leadership,' in the church?

Chapter 26: Setting Up the Conversation:
1. How do you react to the different styles of the Black and White stories?
2. What do you think of the structure for the joint meeting?

Chapter 27: The Third Round of Questions:
1. How do you react to the suggested form of Active Listening?
2. How might you facilitate the conversation between the Black and White participants?

Chapter 28: The Summaries Come In:
1. Fill out the graph yourself and compare to the two churches.
2. Is technology a practical solution to facilitate the large conversation?

Chapter 29: The Celebration Conversation:
1. Are you surprised at the comparison of the two church graphs?
2. Is Craddock's offer like a symbolic from of reparation? What types might you suggest?

Chapter 30: Telling a New Story:
1. Would you be interested in following a similar process in a congregation?
2. If a guidebook would help, look for Racism and God's Grace: Truth and Reconciliation for American Churches.

Printed in the USA
CPSIA information can be obtained
at www.ICGtesting.com
JSHW020857070424
60728JS00001B/1